My Miraculous Survival After Sepsis

Joyce Oluwole

ISBN: 978-1-9162462-0-1

First published 2019

Disclaimer

Every effort has been made to ensure that the information in this book is correct at the time of publication. The author and publisher do not assume and hereby disclaim any liability to any party for any loss, damage, or disruption caused by errors or omissions, whether such errors or omissions result from negligence, accident, or any other cause. This book is not intended as a substitute for the advice of medical professionals, including mental health professionals. The reader should regularly consult a health professional in matters relating to his/ her health, and particularly with respect to any symptoms that may require diagnosis, medical or psychological attention.

For my loving husband Sola, and our wonderful children.

Foreword

Over the course of my publishing and business career, I have met an enormous variety of people. It's true that every person has a story to tell – and I take enormous pleasure in helping them to do this. However, in all my years of publishing, meeting people, and hearing the journey that they've taken, I have never met anyone quite like Joyce. Her story is a testament to the indomitable human spirit and will to survive. Joyce has been through hardships that most of us cannot even conceive of, and yet here she is – with a fully written book and a relentlessly positive approach to life.

Helping Joyce to publish this work has been a thoroughly educational experience. I will confess, I knew almost nothing about sepsis before meeting Joyce, and I believe that the same is true for most people. This book is more than a story, it's a weapon in our fight against one of the most deadly and ignored conditions in the world today, and I encourage any person reading this to spread the word. Share it with your friends and family – so that others will avoid the same hardships that Joyce has so admirably faced.

Whether you are a sufferer of sepsis, know someone who has had the condition, or just want to educate yourself, I guarantee that you will find value and hope in Joyce's words. Joyce is an incredible woman, and her story should serve as inspiration for us all.

Richard McMunn, Bestselling Author and Publisher

Contents

Introduction 11

Why I Wrote This Book 15

Chapter 1 – My Story 19

Chapter 2 – About Sepsis 25

Chapter 3 – Post Sepsis Syndrome (PSS) 43

Chapter 4 – My Coma 49

Chapter 5 – My Husband Sola – in all of this 61

Chapter 6 – Family and Friends 79

Chapter 7 – Home After 9 Months In Hospital 151

Chapter 8 – I Can Do It 165

Chapter 9 – Venturing Out 177

Chapter 10 – Life After Sepsis 187

Chapter 11 – A Dream Come True 203

Chapter 12 – Personalised Bible Verses 211

Chapter 13 – A Harvest Of Motivational Thoughts 223

Chapter 14 – GOFUNDME 227

Acknowledgements 230

Introduction

Hello, and thank you for picking up a copy of this book. The purpose of this book is to share my experiences and to encourage all readers, able-bodied and otherwise, to put their trust in God – whatever their circumstances. I truly believe that He will come through for you, one way or another. He will never leave you, whatever your situation. With faith, you will always be able to draw upon that higher power, whenever you need it, for comfort, peace, and strength.

This was not an easy book to write. However, my friends, family, nurses, and even the people I have bumped into on the street, have inspired and encouraged me.

One thing that all of these people have in common, is that they marvel at my attitude in spite of my disabilities. They always ask me how I cope, and how I feel about losing my legs and seven fingers. I tell them plainly that I don't think about my disabilities. To be honest, I just haven't been able to dwell on them. Naturally, negative thoughts occasionally pass through my mind – but these are fleeting at most. This attitude is definitely by the grace of God. In truth, I am too busy trying to be my old self, and yearning to do the things I did prior to my illness. These days, I don't worry anywhere near as much as I did before I fell ill. I am more patient, and more relaxed. I have experienced some of the worst things that life has to offer, but I am strong, and I have maintained my sense of self. In this book, I narrate my story – from the day I fell ill on April 1st 2015, to date. I give details of my illness, and the causes and symptoms to look out for. There is a vivid recollection of my comatose state while I was on admission in the hospital. My friends and family have also made valuable contributions about how they coped when they learnt about my illness. I also quote personalised Bible verses, which held me in good stead during my illness, and continue to show me that God had a reason for sparing my life. Likewise, he had a reason for healing me, and for making me stronger every day.

It is my fervent hope that by sharing my story with you, you will be encouraged – regardless of whether you have a disability or not.

Mine was indeed a miraculous survival. When the doctors reached the end of their tether and said that there was nothing more they could do for me, my Father, my Creator, took over. He brought me back to life, because my time was not yet up. I have no legs, and several amputated fingers, but I am still alive; God has something more for me to do before He calls me home. While I was on the mend, I always prayed, asking God to show what He wanted of me. Now, I ask Him to give me the power to do this, in whatever time I have left.

Research shows that people who have suffered from sepsis have a two to seven-year life span, because of complications surrounding the condition. Yet, here I am.

My story is a testimony to God's greatness and goodness. If He did it for me, He will do it for you also. Believe in Him and have faith.

My philosophy is that death does not come easy. Hence, as long as one is alive, one should make the most of it. Do not die before death comes. If you are ill, God will either heal you or give you the strength that you need to carry on until He calls you home. If, by His grace, you are in good health, but the stresses of life are getting you down, then you need to draw closer to Him. He will give you the relief that you need.

In my case, I am determined to make the most of whatever time I have left. I have a young daughter who needs her mother, and who always says she wants to sit on my lap. I explained that she can't do that for now, but I am looking forward to the time when my stumps will be strong enough to take her weight!

It has been a rollercoaster journey for me since April 1st, 2015. Thank God nobody thought I was pulling a fast one on April Fools' Day! I was in and out of hospital admissions until September 2017. Each time, God healed me.

I pray that my story will inspire, encourage, and motivate you. There is no safer place to put your trust, than with God.

God bless you. Amen.

Why I Wrote This
Book

I wrote this book first and foremost as a testimony of my faith, to show that, with God, nothing is impossible. It was only through God's mercy that I was miraculously brought back to life from the brink of death. And so I want to encourage readers of this book to put their faith and trust in Almighty God, whatever their circumstances may be. He will come through for them. The second objective of this book is to make people aware of the dreaded illness known as sepsis. Sepsis does not care who you are. It comes like a thief in the night, attacking children and adults alike, everywhere and anywhere. Hundreds of thousands of people all over the world have died or suffered severe disabilities from this disease, because of their ignorance of its symptoms, which are similar to common illnesses.

Thirdly, I want people to know that anyone who survives this uncommon illness **can** make a full recovery and, indeed, have a good life after sepsis.

- They can do most, if not all, the things they did before the illness.

- They can work towards, and aim for, higher horizons.

- They can, and will, surprise themselves at what they achieve.

This book is not just my story, but the stories of my friends and loved ones, who also suffered as a result of my illness. It's important to understand that each person had a different experience. Therefore, within these stories, you may see small variations upon what each person went through and perceived.

Joyce Oluwole

Chapter 1 –

My Story

On April 1st, 2015, I woke up feeling out of sorts. I felt that there was something wrong, but I couldn't put my finger on what it was. I had the urge to go to the surgery (the doctor's office) to see my doctor, but I didn't know what I would tell him. After all, even I didn't know what was wrong with me.

I drove hurriedly to the surgery with my husband sitting next to me in the car. When we arrived, I was reminded that I couldn't see any doctor there without having a prior appointment. I was instead advised to go to the Accident & Emergency (A&E) department at St George's Hospital.

When we arrived at the hospital, we had to queue before we could speak to the nurse on the reception desk. While in the queue, I bent over, and suddenly began to sway from side to side with my arms raised up in front me. Then I fell to the ground. Two nurses helped me to get up, while another one brought a wheelchair for me to sit in. I felt better after I sat down in the chair. I asked the nurses if I could go back and take my place in the queue, since I was feeling better sitting in the wheelchair. They refused, and I was taken to a cubicle where some blood was taken from my arm for testing. The result of the blood test showed that there was an infection somewhere in my body. My CRP (inflammatory factors), as it is called, was 100%.

Following this, I was then moved to a ward upstairs. I decided to phone two friends using the hospital phone, and told them that I was on admission at the hospital. They visited me promptly. We talked and joked, and I told them that I was still waiting for a diagnosis of what was wrong with me. Then I told one of them that I would like to eat a traditional meal called eba (made from cassava) with apon stew (made from melon seed). My friends went and fetched these for me, and I enjoyed the meal very much.

However, within ten minutes of eating, I went into a coma. Sores began to erupt on my toes, until they started to dangle from my foot. The doctors were called to my bed, but they didn't know what was wrong. They only told my husband that they might need to amputate my toes. Soon the sores began to spread to my legs and torso. I had multiple organ failures, and septic shock. I was now on a life support machine, and I was given strong antibiotics intravenously. My husband said the doctors were baffled, and they told him that they were still trying to find the cause of the illness. Other doctors were invited in, but no one knew what I had. This period of indecision went on for several weeks, with the doctors doing all they could to try and save my life.

Finally, it was discovered that I had sepsis of the blood, of unknown cause. To this day, they have never discovered the exact cause of the illness. My hospital file states that I had "sepsis of unknown cause".

Two years later, I attended the same hospital to have my amputated stumps dressed, when my eye caught a poster which stated: "Could it be sepsis? Ask your doctor" followed by a list of symptoms. I thought this was strange, and thought to myself that the doctor should know if his patient had sepsis or any other disease. When I read the rest of the poster, my curiosity turned to anger.

The symptoms for sepsis were described as:

- Slurred speech;

- Extreme shivering or muscle pain;

- Passing no urine (in a whole day);

- Severe breathlessness;

- Mottled or discoloured skin;

- Feeling as if you might die.

I hadn't had any of the above symptoms before I was admitted to the hospital. So, I assumed that I had contracted the condition whilst at the hospital. I immediately went straight to the reception desk, and informed the ladies working there of my thoughts. I was visibly annoyed. The nurses pacified me, explaining that the poster was a new thing. It felt to me as if the medical profession had only just discovered the symptoms of sepsis, even though the ailment had been around for a long time. If I hadn't contracted sepsis whilst in the hospital, then where could it possibly have come from? I pondered over this while I was waiting for my stumps to be dressed, still feeling angry and upset. Then, I suddenly snapped out of it. I told myself that doctors are only human. They can't be expected to know everything. What they know is what God has revealed to them. Period!

When I first stepped into the A&E department of St George's, in April 2015, I felt a sense of relief. I knew that I was in the right place at the right time, and that everything would be fine from that moment onwards. Little did I know, however, that I would be in that same hospital for the next 7 months, and after that would spend another 2 months and 12 days at another hospital. It was only on December 17th, 2015, that I was finally allowed to return home – to spend Christmas with my family.

Chapter 2 –

About Sepsis

One of the biggest issues that I had trouble coming to terms with, was the seeming lack of knowledge and understanding from the medical professionals who treated me, in regard to sepsis. Although the majority of these people did their absolute best, it is still not known how or why I contracted the illness, and likely it will remain a mystery.

In this book, I don't just want to share my story and encourage you, but I also want to spread awareness about sepsis, the complications surrounding the illness, and educate readers about the warning signs. So, in this chapter, I will provide you with some essential information, so that you (I pray) will never have to go through what I did.

What is Sepsis?
Sepsis is a life-threatening condition that arises when the body's response to infection causes injury to its own tissues and organs. The condition develops when the chemicals that the immune system releases into the bloodstream to fight an infection instead cause inflammation throughout the entire body. Common signs and symptoms include fever, increased heart rate, increased breathing rate, and confusion. Sepsis can take place in any part of the body. The most commonly affected areas are the lungs, urinary tract, stomach, and pelvis.

Sometimes, sepsis can appear as "flu-like" symptoms, as a chest infection, or as gastroenteritis. If you have any of the following symptoms, then it is advised that you seek immediate medical attention:

- Slurred speech or confusion;
- Mottled or discoloured skin;
- Passing no urine (in a day);
- Extreme shivering or muscle pain;
- Feeling as if you are going to die;
- Severe breathlessness.

Without quick treatment, sepsis can lead to multiple organ failure and death. So, it's essential that you deal with it fast, and recognise the symptoms. Don't just take my word for it; it's important to understand how serious this condition is, from the words of trained medical professionals. The following is sourced directly from Sepsis-NHS.UK:

Types of infection associated with sepsis include:

- Lung infection (pneumonia);
- Appendicitis;
- An infection of the thin layer of tissue that lines the inside of the abdomen (peritonitis);
- An infection of the bladder, urethra, or kidneys (urinary tract infection);
- An infection of the gallbladder (cholecystitis) or bile ducts (cholangitis);
- Skin infections, such as cellulitis – this can be caused by an intravenous catheter that's been inserted through the skin to give fluids or medication;

- Infections after surgery;
- Infections of the brain and nervous system – such as meningitis or encephalitis;
- Flu (in some cases);
- Bone infection (osteomyelitis);
- Heart infection (endocarditis).

Sometimes, the specific infection and source of sepsis can't be identified. Mine was not identified for several weeks.

What causes the symptoms of sepsis?

Usually, your immune system keeps an infection limited to one place. This is known as a localised infection. Your body produces white blood cells, which travel to the site of the infection to destroy the germs causing infection. A series of biological processes then occur, such as tissue swelling, which help fight the infection and prevent it spreading. This process is known as inflammation.

If your immune system is weak or an infection is particularly severe, it can quickly spread through the blood into other parts of the body. This causes the immune system to go into overdrive, and the inflammation affects the entire body. This can cause more problems than the initial infection, as widespread inflammation damages tissue and interferes with blood flow. Furthermore, the interruption in blood flow leads to a dangerous drop in blood pressure, which stops oxygen reaching your organs and tissues.

As I mentioned before, I had none of these symptoms prior to my admission into hospital. I have only now just found out that it is possible to get sepsis without any symptoms or identifiable causes, but an infection is detectable when tests are done at the hospital.

Sepsis is no respecter of persons, and it can affect babies, children, youths, adults, and the elderly – practically anyone and everyone. Even more scary is the fact that one can get sepsis more than once. I was told recently that I had sepsis more than once while on admission, which is why I spent seven months at St George's Hospital.

Despite all of this, there is yet hope. Medical centres across the UK are spreading awareness of the condition, via posters and campaigns. There is also significant research taking place, in particular at Strathclyde University in Glasgow, where they have developed an innovative, low cost test for early diagnosis of sepsis, which could save thousands of lives. In simple terms, this involves using a tiny needle to detect if one of the protein biomarkers of sepsis – interleukin-6 – is present in the bloodstream. The small size of the needles makes them ideal for initial testing, and presents a much quicker test timeframe than currently existing hospital tests, which can sometimes take up to 72 hours to process. The needle shape of the device also means that it can be implanted and used on patients in intensive care.

Currently, the research for this project is in an early stage. The team in question is hoping to attract more funding to take the project through to clinical trials and further testing – but this is an extremely positive step!

Sepsis the Killer

According to the UK Sepsis Trust, an estimated 52,000 people die from sepsis every year in the UK alone, and six million people die every year across the globe as a result of the condition. However, with early diagnosis, and the right treatment, the majority of people infected with sepsis make a full recovery. Without early treatment and diagnosis, the condition leads to multiple organ failure and death. A delay of just one hour can sharply increase the chances of fatality.

When sepsis is diagnosed, this is usually done by taking simple bodily measurements – measuring factors like temperature, heart rate, and breathing rate, as well as studying the results of blood tests. This is why diagnosing the condition can sometimes take as long as 72 hours – there is a reliance on clinical judgement and hospital laboratory techniques to diagnose the condition. The blood test in particular is very laborious, as the results need to go through a computer, to a laboratory, and then be processed prior to the result. Hence, the techniques being developed at Strathclyde University could be a serious game changer – not just in the UK but globally too. The UK Sepsis Trust believes that earlier diagnosis and treatment in the UK alone would save at least 14,000 lives a year – so if you magnify this to the rest of the world then you can start to see just how much of an impact it could have.

Sepsis Around The World

As part of my own efforts to spread awareness about this terrible condition, I have done research into the impact that sepsis has on people across the planet. Below are my findings:

Britain

As of 2018, it has been estimated that sepsis death rates in Britain are approximately five times higher than the best-performing countries in Europe. In essence, the UK is failing to keep up with other nations in terms of their treatment and medical care of sepsis patients.

Poland

Severe sepsis was observed in one-fourth of patients treated in ICUs (intensive care units) in Poland. However, the actual number of severe sepsis patients is at least 2 times higher, because many patients with severe sepsis were treated outside accredited ICUs. Severe sepsis constitutes a major health problem in Poland.

Severe sepsis in intensive care units in Poland--a point prevalence study in 2012 and 2013. (Kübler A1, Adamik B, Ciszewicz-Adamiczka B, Ostrowska E).

Netherlands

The most severe sepsis patients in the Netherlands were admitted to the ICU due to acute infection (62%) or after acute surgery. Severe sepsis mostly originated from a respiratory (47%) or abdominal infection (34%). The estimated incidence of patients admitted to ICUs with severe sepsis in the Netherlands was 8,643 per year.

Prevalence and incidence of severe sepsis in Dutch intensive care units. (Van Gestel A1, Bakker J, Veraart CP, van Hout BA).

Turkey

The respiratory system (71.6%) was the most common site of infection, and Acinetobacter spp. (33.7%) were the most common isolated pathogen. Approximately, 74.9%, 39.1%, and 26.5% of Acinetobacter, Klebsiella, and Pseudomonas spp. isolates, respectively, were carbapenem-resistant, which was not associated with a higher mortality risk. Age, acute physiology and chronic health evaluation II score at ICU admission, sequential organ failure assessment score on study day, solid organ malignancy, presence of severe sepsis or shock, Candida spp. infection, renal replacement treatment, and a nurse-to-patient ratio of 1:4 (compared with a nurse-to-patient ratio of 1:2) were independent predictors of mortality in infected patients.

A high prevalence of sepsis and an unacceptably high mortality rate were observed in Turkish ICUs. Although the prevalence of carbapenem resistance was high in Turkish ICUs, it was not associated with a higher risk for mortality.

Epidemiology of sepsis in intensive care units in Turkey: a multicenter, point-prevalence study. (Baykara N1, Akalın H2, Arslantaş MK3, Hancı V4, Çağlayan Ç5, Kahveci F6, Demirağ K7, Baydemir C8, Ünal N9; Sepsis Study Group.)

Africa

Sepsis is a leading cause of morbidity and mortality worldwide and particularly in Africa where awareness is low and resources are limited. There are limited reports on the epidemiology, management and outcomes of the sepsis syndromes from Africa, but below I have accumulated as much information as possible.

Nigeria

A study among patients of South East Nigeria as reported on 23/5/17 revealed that out of 4199 admissions, 311 were diagnosed with sepsis. The majority of patients had co-morbid illnesses with diabetes and HIV as the commonest conditions as well as respiratory, urogenital diseases. In conclusion, sepsis remains an important cause of admissions among medical patients in Nigeria and the associated in-hospital mortality is high. The predictors of in-hospital mortality were analysed and should be used to improve sepsis management.

The prevalence of comorbidities among people living with HIV in Brent: a diverse London Borough. (Ava Lorenc, Piriyankan Ananthavarathan, corresponding author James Lorigan, Mohamade Jowata, and Gary Brook.)

Angola, South Africa, Kenya, Malawi, Zimbabwe, Ghana, Nigeria

The aforementioned countries appear to have a high incidence of neonatal sepsis. Neonatal sepsis refers specifically to a bacterial blood stream infection within newborn babies – such as meningitis or pneumonia – and fever. This is one of the common reasons for why newborns are admitted to intensive units within developing countries, and contributes strongly to the mortality rate of newborns within these countries – as well as in developed countries too.

South Africa

Group B Streptococcus (GBS) is a major cause of morbidity and mortality, and is one of the commonest causes of invasive infection among newborns worldwide. African countries like Kenya, South Africa, Zimbabwe and Malawi have however reported high rates of GBS sepsis.

Aetiology of neonatal sepsis in Nigeria, and relevance of Group b streptococcus: A systematic review. (Nubwa Medugu, Kenneth Iregbu, Pui-Ying Iroh Tam, and Stephen Obaro.)

Brazil

Within Brazilian ICUs, sepsis is the leading cause of death. Sepsis has a 55.7% mortality rate – an astonishing figure really. Surveys conducted have shown that more than 230,000 adults die from sepsis in Brazilian ICUs every single year. This is a real indication of the scale of the problem, and a devastating yearly loss of life.

Australia

In Australia, sepsis is known as "the silent killer". There are approximately 18,000 diagnosed cases of sepsis in Australia per year, and the condition kills sufferers at a rate of 5000 per year. This is equal to more than one person every two hours. And yet, approximately 40% of all Australians haven't even heard of the disease. While there are drives in place to spread awareness, medical officials have confessed that more needs to be done to combat this deadly condition.

India

In India, approximately 34% of sepsis patients die in the ICU every year. And yet, there are an estimated 200 cases of sepsis reported every single month. Sepsis is one of the most common, life-threatening infections in the country, but still not enough is being done to tackle this. With various locations in India suffering from poverty and poor medical care, there are people within the country who will be under-equipped for treatment, for a long time to come.

China

Although the rate of mortality related to sepsis has significantly declined in the developed countries, the issue is still a concern. Due to increased incidences, the number of sepsis-related mortality cases is considerably high. In addition, the long-term mortality rate is not optimistic, and an increasing number of sepsis survivors are faced with a poor quality of life. On the other hand, the mortality of sepsis in developing countries, which occupy most of the world's population, remains high or may be rendered such due to the lack of epidemiological data. China is a distinct country, which has more than 1.3 billion people, occupies a huge land mass, and experiences extremely rapid economic development, yet has relatively slow medical health care system evolvement.

The following reasons may contribute to the high mortality rate of severe sepsis in mainland China: (I) treatment delay. For treatment of sepsis, time is pivotal. The most efficient way to improve prognosis is to complete the initial resuscitation bundles in the first few hours after the onset of sepsis. However, due to the lack of early triage of sepsis system, limited ICU resources, and low-to-high level hospital medical visiting system, many septic patients might lose the precious period when they can receive intensive care management. The efficacy of thymosin alpha 1 for severe sepsis (ETASS) study conducted in Guangdong province, an economically developed region in mainland China, reported that the median time when the patient developed first organ failure and enrolment was 28 and 42 hrs, respectively in the control and treatment groups. While the data from our sepsis database represents the economically less developed area, more than 60% of the severe sepsis patients developed organ failure after more than 48 hrs upon ICU admission. Most of them revealed a history of treatment in other hospitals before sepsis aggravation; poor compliance of sepsis bundle.

Current epidemiology of sepsis in mainland China.(Xuelian Liao,1 Bin Du,2 Meizhu Lu,1 Minming Wu,1 and Yan Kang.)

Qatar

In Qatar, significant in-roads have been made in an attempt to educate people about the severity of blood poisoning. Approximately 5,000 people in Qatar contract sepsis every year, and around 20% of these people die from the condition. New programmes are being set up to act as a "safety net", which will educate medical professionals and citizens alike – making them more aware of the symptoms – thereby aiming to reduce deaths from sepsis by 25% across the next five years.

How To Prevent The Occurrence Of Sepsis

Many infections can be prevented simply by good and consistent hygiene. Others can be prevented through the use of vaccinations.

Sepsis.org, one of the leading bodies in the fight against this deadly disease, provide the following advice:

Vaccinations

Viral infections, such as influenza (the flu), chicken pox, and HIV, are caused by viruses. Viruses are microscopic organisms that must live inside a living host, such as humans. Although each virus is different, viruses generally don't survive for long outside the host.

Usually, when you have a viral illness, your body produces antibodies that keep you from getting the illness again – they make you immune. Vaccines have been developed for many viruses, such as chicken pox (varicella), tetanus, and polio. These vaccines, sometimes called immunisations, trick your body into thinking that it has been infected with the virus – which then makes you immune to actually getting the illness.

Caring for wounds

Every cut, scrape, or break in the skin can allow bacteria to enter your body – and it is this bacteria that causes infections. For this reason, it's essential that all wounds be cleaned as quickly as possible and be kept clean. They should also be monitored for signs of an infection.

Cleaning open wounds:

- Always wash your hands before touching an open wound. If possible, wear clean disposable gloves.

- If the wound is deep, gaping, or has jagged edges and can't be closed easily, it may need stitches. If so, see your healthcare provider as soon as possible.

- If the wound does not appear to need stitches, rinse it and the surrounding area with clean (not soapy) water. Gently running water over the wound can help remove any dirt or debris that may be inside. If you believe that there is still debris in the wound, this should be checked by a healthcare provider.

- If desired, apply an antibiotic cream or ointment.

- Cover the wound to protect it from dirt if necessary.

- Watch for signs of infection – redness around the wound, skin around the wound warm to touch, increased pain, and/or discharge from the wound. Consult your physician or nurse practitioner if you suspect you may have an infection.

- If you have a blister, do not pop it or break it. The blister is a protective barrier and breaking it introduces an opening in your skin. If the blister does break, keep the area clean and monitor for signs of infection.

Bacterial infections

Bacteria can cause infections in many parts of the body, and can enter through a variety of means – such as a cut or bug bite on your arm, your kidneys or bladder, or even your lungs (pneumonia). If you have been diagnosed with a bacterial infection, you will likely be prescribed antibiotics for treatment. Antibiotics are medications that kill bacteria or stop them from reproducing.

Some antibiotics work against several types of bacteria, while others are for specific bacteria only. Partly because of overuse and misuse of these medications, some bacteria are becoming resistant to certain antibiotics. This is making it harder to treat infections. For this reason, it is essential that people take antibiotics only when necessary and exactly as prescribed.

What to do when you are prescribed antibiotics:

- Follow the instructions regarding how the medication should be taken – with or without food, before or after meals.
- Take it on time (example: once a day, every six hours).

- Finish the full course (7 days, 10 days, etc.), even if you feel better sooner. The symptoms will disappear before the bacteria have been completely eliminated.

- Store the antibiotics as directed, to preserve their strength.

What not to do with antibiotics:

- Do not ask your physician or nurse practitioner for a prescription for an infection not caused by bacteria. Antibiotics do not work on viruses, such as colds or the flu, or other illnesses not caused by bacteria.

- Do not take someone else's antibiotics, even if you do have a bacterial infection. It may not be the correct type or dosage, or it may have expired. It can be dangerous to take expired antibiotics.

Viral infections

- Most viral infections run their course without treatment, but some viral infections may be treated with anti-viral medications. If you are ill and don't seem to be getting better, are getting worse or are developing new symptoms, are having difficulty breathing, or are concerned, please consult your healthcare professional. Sometimes, medications may be prescribed for the symptoms caused by the virus.

- Fungal and parasitic infections.

- Infections caused by fungi or parasites must be treated with specific medications that will eliminate the cause.

Hand washing

- Washing our hands is a simple task that we all do every day, several times a day. However, for hand washing to be effective, it needs to be done properly and possibly more frequently than many people do already.

- Generally, to wash your hands well, you simply need to use running water (to help wash the debris from your hands), lather your hands well (making sure to rub between each finger and under your nails), and dry your hands thoroughly with a clean towel.

- If you are using a hand sanitiser (waterless cleanser), use the same motions of rubbing your hands together, in between your fingers and remembering the tops of your hands and your thumbs. Your hands should be dry before touching objects.

If you're wondering whether to use a waterless cleanser or soap and water, the general belief is that soap and water are best for hands that are visibly dirty, or after activities, such as toileting. Hand sanitisers are good for when hands are not visibly dirty, but you know they need to be cleaned.

Chapter 3 –

Post Sepsis Syndrome (PSS)

Having survived sepsis, one would have thought that just making a speedy recovery from the trauma caused by this dreaded illness, is all that would be needed. But no, a new battle begins – with what is termed as Post Sepsis Syndrome (PSS).

Post-sepsis syndrome is a condition that affects up to 50% of sepsis survivors. They are left with physical and/ or psychological long-term effects, such as insomnia, difficulty getting to sleep, or staying asleep. They may also suffer nightmares, vivid hallucinations and panic attacks.

Some sepsis survivors experience a variety of physical, psychological and emotional problems while recovering. This usually lasts between 6 and 18 months, sometimes longer.

Because you may look well, others (including your employer, doctor, or family) may be unaware of the problems and expect you to be better now. Don't suffer in silence. Tell them about PSS and how it's affecting you.

Below are some of the common symptoms of PSS:

- Lethargy / excessive tiredness;

- Poor mobility / muscle weakness;

- Breathlessness / chest pains;

- Swollen limbs (excessive fluid in the tissues);

- Joint and muscle pains;

- Insomnia;

- Hair loss;

- Dry / flaking skin and nails;

- Taste changes;

- Poor appetite;

- Changes in vision;

- Changes in sensation in limbs;

- Repeated infections from the original site or a new infection;

- Reduced kidney function;

- Feeling cold;

- Excessive sweating.

The psychological and emotional symptoms of PSS include:

- Anxiety / fear of sepsis recurring;

- Depression;

- Flashbacks;

- Nightmares;

- Insomnia (due to stress or anxiety);

- PTSD (Post Traumatic Stress Disorder);

- Poor concentration;

- Short term memory loss;

- Mood swings.

What treatment is available?

There is no specific treatment for PSS, but most people will get better with time. In the meantime, it's a case of managing the individual problems and looking after yourself while you are recovering.

Tell your family and friends about PSS, explain how you feel and give them information to read so they can understand what you're going through. It will help you all get through this difficult time.

Not all doctors know about PSS. So, it is important that your doctor assesses your symptoms and excludes any other causes of the problems. Your doctor may refer you to a different professional to help manage individual PSS problems, such as a pain specialist to manage your pain, a counsellor or psychiatrist to manage mental health and emotional problems, or a physio or occupational therapist to manage fatigue. Above all, remind yourself that, horrible as PSS is, you're not alone, and these problems are part of the recovery process. Sometimes you have to look back to where you started, to see how far you have come.

Recurring infections

Some survivors find that their immune system is not as effective in the year following their sepsis. As a result, they get one infection after another, whether it's coughs and colds, repeated water infections or a recurring wound infection.

This can be worrying, as many people fear that they may get sepsis again. In most cases, early medical consultation and treatment with antibiotics treat the infection and it doesn't progress to anything worse. But it's important not to neglect any infections. Always make sure you, and those close to you, know the signs of sepsis and seek urgent medical attention if concerned.

In summary

I hope that this chapter has provided you with some useful information about sepsis, its causes, symptoms, and how you can get engaged and help to spread awareness. This isn't just a book about my story – it's about you, your loved ones, and the people around you. It's about us all working together to fight this awful condition, and educate the world on how serious sepsis is.

Chapter 4 –

My Coma

I have a very vivid recollection of most of the things that happened to me during my comatose state – where I went and what I did. In this chapter, I will describe everything that went on inside my mind, whilst the doctors were battling to save my life.

My first trip was to a hospital in Germany. I was in a long queue. We were all waiting to be treated, and it felt like a lifetime. Then, suddenly, a doctor wearing a white gown approached me and pushed me forward to be signed in. He said he would help me to get better. He pushed me past many patients, and brought me to a very big ward consisting of people with various ailments. He carried out various tests on me, in order to detect my illness, but he couldn't find the cause of my illness. Meanwhile, I told him that I felt very ill inside, but didn't know exactly what was wrong with me nor the cause of my illness.

Following this, the man left the ward, and I never saw him again. Next, I found myself in Milan, trying to get to a hospital – but I had a lot of problems at the airport. They wouldn't let me in, because I was in a hospital bed, which was too wide to get through their gates. They said I had to come off the bed in order to get out of the airport. I told the officials that I was too weak to walk. They helped me to phone a hospital, but the hospital said that they had not been informed about any patient coming from Germany, and so I was put back on a plane. I didn't know where the plane was going, but it finally landed in Ghana – my mother's place of origin. Here I felt very relieved that I would get the treatment that I needed, and that they would be able to diagnose my illness. By this time, I was very tired, weak, and hungry.

My next problem was to locate my mother's family home, known as Lutterodt Hall in Osu, Accra. Someone was helping to push me around in the hospital bed. We moved from one street to another, until I located the house.

I only recognised it from the name written outside. It had been renovated and painted white inside and outside. When I entered, I could see that it had become a medical research centre. Everything was sparkling clean and white. It was like a labyrinth, with winding stairs on one side and a very long and winding ramp on the other.

I looked around in wonder. I couldn't see anyone, but I heard the sound of machines in the background, so I waited after getting on the ramp in my bed with my "pusher" – the person who pushed me around everywhere. I never saw my "pusher", but I was moving around. As I descended the ramp, I met a bespectacled woman, who asked me what I was looking for. I told her that I was ill and needed urgent care. She then directed me to a room with silver walls. As I approached the reception, a robot came along and asked me what I needed. I answered and said, "I am sick and I want to be healed."

The robot asked, in a male voice, 'Who sent you to the Hall?'

I said, 'This is my grandfather's house.' I felt sure that I would get some help here.

The robot replied, 'Can you identify your grandfather?' I said, 'Yes, I can, if I see a photo of him.' The robot brought out a photo, and I recognised it as the same picture that hangs in my father's living room to this day.

Next, the robot asked me if I knew my grandfather's name. I said that I didn't. By this time, I had become agitated, and wondered when I would get treated and be given some food.

The robot said my great-grandfather was a Dutchman, and had come to the Gold Coast to mine gold. I informed the robot that I knew this already, and asked if I could see a doctor. His response was that money from the gold mine had been used to build this magnificent medical research centre, and that as I was a descendant, I would get treated without having to pay. I thanked him, and I was finally taken into the theatre, by other robots. I was too scared to ask why I couldn't be seen by a human being. I just knew that I wanted to be made well again. That was my only concern. I left Ghana, not completely healed, but happy to have visited my mother's roots.

I came back to London, and found myself at a friend's home. I was aware that preparations were going on for her son's wedding, because we had talked about it before. Suddenly, another friend appeared, and said someone had to go down what looked like a bottomless pit to sort things out for the wedding. The friend whose son was getting married said that person had to be Joyce.

The floor beneath my feet suddenly split open, and I fell right through. I was very, very scared when I reached the bottom.

Next, I found myself in what looked like a grandiose palace. It was the home of a caliphate. I was taken in and told to prepare the large lounges for the wedding guests. I got to work with decorations. After I finished, two ladies came in and told me that the bride-to-be was very tired, so I would have to take her place for a particular ceremony. I wasn't given a choice; I was just ordered to do things. I was then dressed up in flowing white and gold robes, and I was attached to a wall. I was rotated around upside down on the wall, and I sang as visitors trooped in. Finally, the bride and groom arrived, and I was brought down from the wall. The groom, my friend's son, thanked me heartily for helping his bride out.

Following this, I was told to arrange the bride's clothes and get them ready for her to change into. I did so, and then left. When I got outside, my friend asked me to stay and help her clean up the house after the guests had left. I obliged her. When we finished cleaning up, I told her that I needed to get back to the hospital. So, we parted ways.

I found myself back in my hospital bed at St George's. Here, I was taken to an underground ward. It was always dark in the ward, and one could see the shadows of nurses milling around. They didn't talk much to me. They only administered my medication and left. At night I couldn't sleep and just waited for the rays of light to come in at daybreak. One night, I told a nurse that I was always afraid because it was so dark in the room.

She looked at me, without an ounce of sympathy on her face. 'That's just the way it is, I'm afraid,' she said.

One day I was moved to what seemed to be another part of the hospital. Here, there were two nuns waiting for me. My bed was pushed towards them. The next thing I knew, they began to untie the white bandages that were all over my body. I asked them why they were removing the bandages, and they said they had been instructed to remove them because I was no longer a Catholic. I told them that I was never a Catholic, although I attended a Catholic school for my A-Levels. They insisted that I was a Catholic, and that they had to remove the robes of Catholicism from me. I told them that my mother was a Catholic and not me. I told them that I was chapel prefect at school, and I only prepared what was needed for Mass and ensured that students entered the chapel in an orderly fashion, and that was as far as my involvement with Catholicism went. I said that I remained an Anglican, and that I had the sisters' permission to go to an Anglican Church outside boarding school after Mass every Sunday.

Despite me saying all this, the nuns continued taking off the bandages. There seemed to be a lot on me. When they finished, I was left with light blue bandages covering my body. The nuns said that I had been stripped of Catholicism, and I would have to reapply if I ever wanted to be a member again.

And yet still, they weren't done. I was already exhausted from the pulling and tugging they did with the bandages, but now they turned to me and asked me what I wanted to do with the estate which my Catholic husband had left for me. I said that my husband was not Catholic, and that he was still alive. Then they told me to look in front of me. There I saw a lady standing far off, just staring at me. I immediately recognised her as someone whom I'd met at The Institute of Bankers dinner, held in 1982. She was Danish. I told the nuns that she was the Catholic man's wife, and that the estate belonged to her and her children, not me. They said she wasn't his wife, but she had borne five children for him while I was married to him, and she was now looking after my son – who was the sixth child.

As you can imagine, I was highly confused by all of this. I told the nuns that they had made a mistake. Their response was that they never made mistakes, but that if I requested so, bequeaths would be done.

When I looked up again, the Danish lady had disappeared. Then I saw the back of the husband they had alluded to. He was a Gambian, but I couldn't see his face. The nuns then bade me goodbye. Some care assistants arrived, whom I recognised as students from my time in health and social care, and I tried to chat with them. However, they didn't respond. They just did their jobs and left.

Later that day, I was moved to what was called an incinerator room at the hospital. I was put on a stretcher and slowly pushed into a tube-like structure. I heard the man operating the structure shout out loud, 'She is not dead yet, come and take her away', and I was pulled out. I then found myself back in Ghana at Lutterodt Hall. This time there were loads of my mother's relations around, several of whom lived on the top floor of the hall.

When I arrived, one of these relatives was complaining bitterly about how she was being treated, and that she didn't have any money to pay to the court on the matter. I told her that I would help out once I got back to England, and was able to earn some money. She suggested that we should go to a restaurant for a meal, and I agreed. As soon as we got past the corridor, I saw a room that had my name on it, and the figures 1795 – the number of the case that had been struck off in court. This was the case that the lady was referring to. She hugged me tightly, and said that the sign indicated that the case was decided in her favour already. I smiled and congratulated her. We had a lovely meal. Thereafter, she would take me along to the shops every day, to do her shopping. We both carried large bags of clothes, and I was always tired. She also asked me to go with her to various parties – at which she enjoyed herself, but I was simply too weak to be happy. When I begged her to help me get back to London, because I was tired and felt sick, she didn't reply. Yet, within a moment, I suddenly found myself back at St George's.

The next day, my husband Sola came to visit me. He said he wanted to take me to Chinatown in Piccadilly Circus. I was very happy at this. We went by bus, got off at Piccadilly Circus, and began to ask for directions to Chinatown. There were so many restaurants, and it was difficult to choose one. We passed by one large restaurant which had a hot spinning wheel outside on its patio. I was curious, so I went near it, and my skirt suddenly got caught in the wheel. I started to scream as I was wheeled around. My husband started to scream too, and called out for help. The workers said they could not stop the wheel until it reached the top floor, where delicacies were served. I was very frightened. However, they went to the top floor and stopped the wheel – I managed to escape with just a few burns. As soon as I was released, my husband hailed a taxi, which took us back to the hospital. We didn't have our Chinese meal after all.

When we got back, no one had missed me. No one knew that I had been out of the hospital for several hours. When the nurses came around to give me my medication, my husband tried to tell them that I had been burnt in a freak accident, but they paid no attention to him. Meanwhile, I was glad to be back in the hospital after my ordeal.

The next day, I went down a tunnel. Approaching me was a boy wearing a bright green aso-oke (a hand-woven cloth).

I immediately recognised him as my son, and I carried him on my shoulder and brought him out of the tunnel. My husband was standing at the edge of the tunnel, and I told him that I had found our son – our young daughter's twin brother. Apparently, he had been adopted by a childless couple. I didn't know how that happened, but I was happy to have him back. I told my husband that I wanted to bring him up with our daughter. He agreed, and I was pleased. However, the following day when my husband visited me in the hospital, he told me that we could not take the child back after all – because he didn't think he would be able to cope looking after two kids. He said that as I was still in hospital he just couldn't handle it, and that I should give the child back to the couple and let them bring him up as their child. I was heartbroken by this. The child often came to visit me in hospital without his adopted parents, and he and my daughter always played together, but neither of them knew that they were twins separated at birth. Eventually, my husband said that the visits had to stop. I had no choice in the matter, since I couldn't look after him being stuck in the hospital.

This scenario stayed with me for months after I came out of my coma, and I actually believed that the boy was my daughter's real-life twin, the twin that didn't fully develop in my womb and so was never born. Now, in real life, I still have a bright green hand-woven cloth which is the exact type of cloth that he was wrapped in.

I went to many other places during my comatose state, but I can no longer recall the details of these. However, I remember very clearly the last episode, as it remained with me for the next 19 months after I came out of my coma. On this day, I was taken back to the "incinerator department" at St George's Hospital, and I was again slowly pushed through a white tube. In this tube, I wore a white sequined dress. My arms were crossed over my chest, and my eyes were closed. I was surrounded by sunflowers, their yellow petals glowing in a very bright and glowing light. I had no more pain and I was happy. Most of all, I had this indescribable peace. I had died. But suddenly, while I was enjoying this wonderful feeling, something or someone pulled me out of the tube, and I woke up. I believe that it was at this point that I came out of my comatose state. Back to life – the real world as it were. It was after this that my two legs were amputated.

For many months, I longed to go back into that tube. But I couldn't go back. I longed daily for that peace and joy that I experienced in my heart on that day. But it never came. I never went back into a coma. However, by the latter part of 2017, I began to be thankful for what He had given me. But at other times, I would be in awe of it all, and be unable to understand why I was so happy even after losing my legs and some digits. I would then quickly snap out of it, and tell myself that it was a gift of grace from my Maker, and so I should not question it, but take it and live a life full of gratitude. I was determined that my survival should be a testimony of the goodness of God to as many people as possible – until He calls me home.

I can confidently say that I now have that same peace and joy, without having to go back into the "white tube". Yes, it is possible, and I no longer have the desire to be in the tube. My experience in my comatose state helped me to understand death, and to not be afraid of it. I know that I died in that state. Since I have experienced death, I am not afraid of it at all. I often hummed the following hymn to myself after I came out of my coma and for many months after I was discharged home from hospital:

'Jesu ye: titi aiye, Eru iku ko bami mo; Jesu ye lat'oni lo, Isa oku ko nipa mo, Alleluya!'

English Translation: 'Jesus lives! Thy terrors now, Can O death, no more appal us; Jesus lives by this we know, Thou O grave, canst not enthral us. Halleluyah!'

People should remember that, regardless of their situation, there will always be someone worse off than them. So, learn to live in the moment, and appreciate all the positive things you have in your life.

Chapter 5 –

My Husband Sola – in all of this

A miracle is defined as "an event not explicable by natural or scientific laws". Such an event may be attributed to a supernatural being (especially a deity, magic, a miracle worker, a saint, or a religious leader). To survive an illness after doctors have pronounced that nothing more can medically be done for the patient, is nothing but a miracle from heaven.

Such was the situation of my wife, Joyce Oluremi Oluwole, during her long battle against the devastating illness of sepsis of the blood. When all seemed lost, our merciful God came through for her. She was snatched from the valley of death, to affirm her faith that nothing is impossible for God.

As the Book of Job exclaimed, "Who can comprehend the thunder of God's power?" God stretches the sky over empty space and hangs the earth on nothing. He wraps the rain in thick clouds, and the clouds don't burst with the weight. He covers the face of the moon, shrouding it with his clouds. He created the horizon when he separated the waters: he set the boundary between day and night. These are just the beginning of all that he does, merely a whisper of his power."

When they witnessed the awesomeness of God's power in Joyce's miraculous survival from sepsis, the doctors at the famous St George's Teaching Hospital in Tooting, London, nicknamed my wife "The Miracle Woman".

One fateful night, in the second month after Joyce had been in a coma, the doctors invited me into a meeting room in the intensive care unit of the hospital. The atmosphere was sombre. The nurse offered me tea and biscuits, which I politely declined. My heart raced through the events of the past six weeks and what this meeting might portend.

The doctors said they wanted to brief me on Joyce's condition. She was very, very unwell, but they still had not been able to diagnose the cause of her grave illness. She was not responding to treatment. Rather, she seemed to be rapidly going downhill. They had therefore come to the conclusion that she may not survive beyond the next 24 hours. They were very sorry to give me the bad news, and suggested that I should go home and prepare our children's minds for the eventuality. If anything happened during the night, they would call me on my mobile phone. I thanked them for all their best efforts to save her life, and said that I believed that God would take over her situation from that point on.

My head was reeling. I went back to Joyce's bedside on groggy legs, placed a hand on her forehead, and prayed. I said, in my heart, 'Heavenly Father, the doctors have told me that they have done their best, and it is impossible for them to save her life, but I have faith that with you, God, nothing is impossible. If it is possible, let THIS CUP pass from Joyce. May thy will be done. Amen.'

I drove home close to midnight. Our son, Ore, who had come home from the University of Birmingham where he was preparing for his final law degree examinations, was still up. I told him that I had a meeting with Mummy's doctors, and they said that her chances of survival were not very good. I told him that we needed to pray for her. And so we did. We begged God to have mercy and save her life.

I had put our seven-year-old daughter Tolulope to bed before going to the hospital earlier in the evening. I peeped into her room. Surprisingly, she opened her eyes. I quietly went in and held her hand. I mouthed the words, 'Pray for Mummy' and she nodded and went back to sleep.

I lay down on my bed fully clothed, drifting in and out of sleep intermittently, with the mobile phone beside me. When my body clock woke me up at 5.45 a.m., I murmured a 'Thank God' and then quickly checked my phone in case I had missed a call whilst I was asleep. There was no missed call from the hospital. The bitter cup of death had passed over Joyce. Hallelujah! A calmness immediately descended upon me. It felt as if I had just woken up from a bad dream. This bad dream started on April 1st 2015. Two days earlier, my wife had woken up complaining about feeling unwell. I thought that she was probably tired because the previous day, Sunday, she had attended a Mothers' Day festivity at a local church – where she worshipped at the invitation of a friend. She could not say exactly what was wrong with her. We decided to go and see a doctor at our GP's surgery. She drove her car, and I accompanied her. Unfortunately, we were told that we could not see a doctor without a prior appointment. So, we drove straight to the A&E at St George's Hospital.

After the usual initial assessment by a nurse, Joyce was seen by a doctor who carried out physical examinations and tests, which all came out negative. She was then advised to come back for a more comprehensive test in seven days' time, if she still felt unwell. The following day, Tuesday, she did not feel any better, but we decided to wait and see what would happen. She had an uncomfortable night. Early on Wednesday morning, we were back at the hospital's A&E.

While the doctors were attending to Joyce, I had to go back home to attend to our little daughter. Joyce phoned me later to say that she had been admitted to a ward at the hospital, and that she had called two of her friends, who had promptly come to visit her. She had requested one of them to go and prepare a favourite Nigerian meal for her; she thoroughly enjoyed this, and seemed to be in good spirits.

When I went to visit later in the day, with the personal items she would need in the hospital, I was shocked to learn that a short time after eating this meal, Joyce had collapsed and lost consciousness. She had suffered multiple organ failure. This is medically called "septic shock", which resulted in her going into a coma. She was immediately moved to the intensive care unit of the hospital.

That day was April 1st, so-called April Fools' Day, and my first thought was that this was some macabre joke. But reality dawned on me when I got to the intensive care ward, to be confronted by an unimaginable sight. There lay Joyce, eerily still in this special bed, her face seemingly drained of life. It was devastating.

Soon after being moved into intensive care, Joyce's body had been hooked onto life support machines, which took over the functions of her failing organs. I was alarmed to see sores begin to erupt on her toes. The doctors immediately began to treat her with strong antibiotics intravenously. At that stage, they said they did not know the cause of her illness, and it was only several weeks later that they identified her illness as sepsis. I had never even heard of this condition before. Thanks to the internet, I was able to Google it and learn about this little-known killer.

Sepsis is a serious complication of an infection. Without quick treatment, sepsis can lead to multiple organ failure and death. It can be triggered by an infection in any part of the body. The most common sites of infection leading to sepsis are the lungs, urinary tract, abdomen, and pelvis. Joyce never had the symptoms commonly associated with the disease, which include fever, increased heart rate, increased breathing rate, and confusion. Up to this day, the cause of my wife's sepsis is still unknown.

Given the fact that someone who drove herself to the hospital only the previous day was now in a coma, on life support machines, with her body beginning to rot at the extremities before our very eyes, people began to speculate. We simply could not work out where it had come from, and it was even more baffling for the fact that such a well-renowned hospital could not identify the cause either. Was this a case of "spiritual attack" or food poisoning, or the superbug MRSA (meticillin-resistant staphylococcus aureus) ravaging some hospitals? The answer was blowing in the wind. But I was more concerned with finding a solution, rather than a reason. Joyce's bloated sores were turning her toes into rotting green vegetables, and defying the strongest antibiotic treatment. The doctors said they might have to amputate the toes, as the sores were beginning to spread to her feet.

In the eighth week of Joyce's illness, she began to come out of the coma, and regained consciousness. However, she had become a ghost of herself. The sores had broken out all over her legs and fingers, which had become twisted like animal claws.

Juggling hospital visits with looking after our seven-year-old daughter, Tolu, was stressful. I stretched out the day with beneficial after-school club activities. These usually ended about 5.30 p.m., giving me time to do two hospital visits during the day. Whenever I picked Tolu up from after-school activities, the first question was always, 'When's Mummy coming back home?' Getting back to an empty home at dinnertime was seldom palatable for her, whatever effort I might make to lighten her mood and incentivise her appetite. She was often distraught and constantly in tears, because she was missing her mother very badly, and could not understand why children were not allowed to enter the hospital wards as I told her. Joyce was missing Tolu even more. It was obvious to me that Joyce's steely resolve to cling to life, was preponderantly because of the children. Tolu was a miracle child – who was born in this same hospital when her mum was 54. Oreoluwa, her older brother, was 16 at the time of Tolu's birth. When Joyce came out of the coma after two months, a photo of Tolu on the wall of her room drew her first smile.

The day I first told Tolu that I would be taking her with me to see Mummy at the hospital, after church on a Sunday, her face lit up in a big smile. However, on the way to the hospital, I noticed that she was becoming quite apprehensive. Upon arriving at Joyce's beside, and hearing Joyce speak in her weak, frail voice, Tolu clung to me. There was doubt in her face. She didn't recognise her mother, and we had to leave quickly, because Tolu was becoming agitated. Despite this, I continued bringing Tolu to visit Joyce every Sunday. She gradually got used to the way Joyce looked, and started looking forward to the weekly visits.

Soon after, Sister Toyin arrived from Nigeria. Toyin is Joyce's big sister, and is eight years older than her. It was a big relief to have her come to share in the burden of looking after Joyce. As a professional occupational therapist herself, and coming from a family of medical professionals, she was a pillar of strength. She was able to alternate with me in visiting and encouraging Joyce in the difficult journey of recovery – as did her immediate older sibling, Freddie, who was disconsolate when he rushed to the hospital and found his sister in a coma. Devastated family members and friends rallied round. Everybody was in shock, but found solace in the power of prayer.

Now, the big decision had been taken by the doctors. With the eruption of life-threatening sores moving up Joyce's legs, all the way to her thighs, the only option left was to amputate.

This was now a matter of life or death. I had no hesitation in agreeing with the doctors' proposal and, in consultation with Joyce and Sister Toyin, I signed the papers for the bilateral amputations. Then followed oscillating moments of doubt as to whether what I had agreed to was the right decision. If I had been in the same situation as Joyce, would I have so readily agreed to have my feet amputated, even if death was the only alternative? It takes courage to think things through so quickly and decide that it is better to live with disabilities, however devastating, for the higher purpose of being there for loved ones. The same courage that Joyce showed in readily agreeing to the amputation of her legs was evident when there was a need to amputate seven of her fingers. Further down the road, two years later, this extended to a second shortening of her stumps. She was going to need a lot of courage to survive.

When Joyce first woke up, it took some time before she became aware of her surroundings.

"Have they done it?" she asked.

I nodded, smiled, and kissed her cold forehead. Her legs had been cut through the knees. The stumps were heavily bandaged, but there was some blood seeping through. Mercifully, massive painkiller drugs had shielded her from intense pain.

The next few weeks were devoted to treating the large wounds on Joyce's stumps, and the damage which the sepsis attack had wrought on her body, while she was in a coma. Her fingers had gone all black and twisted, as had her ears and lips. She'd lost the tip of her tongue, so she couldn't speak properly. Her muscles were wasted, so she couldn't move any part of her body. She was on drips 24/7. But she was alive, thank God.

As you would expect, Joyce's journey of recovery was very slow. According to the medical team, however, she was making good progress every day. Her organs were recovering gradually. Because of the gravity of her illness and the expertise with which it was being managed, I did not even notice when she suffered a stroke. I guess that if a critically ill patient is lying in bed, unable to control their movements, the normal signs and symptoms of a stroke would not be apparent to a non-medical person. The fact that she had suffered a stroke, though a mild one, was made manifest after Joyce was eventually able to speak

– she began to stammer. She later had to undertake a long period of speech therapy to restore her to speech normality.

There were many more new challenges ahead for Joyce. Having laid on her back for several weeks on end, she was in danger of having bed sores. Her body needed to be repositioned many times a day. She was not well enough yet to begin physiotherapy, which would enable her to regain muscle strength and to be able to sit up. That was to come later, and was one of many landmarks on the road to recovery. Soon her organs had recovered fully, and she was taken off life support machines. She was still being fed or hydrated through intravenous drips, but feeding by mouth – starting with liquids – was to follow.

After four months in the intensive care unit, the time came when Joyce was strong enough to be moved from intensive care and delivered to a general ward for her treatment to continue. It was like being born again. Her discharge from the intensive care department was an emotional one. Doctors and nurses gathered around Joyce to rejoice with her, and wish her well on the next stage of her journey to full recovery.

Two senior nurses came from the McEntee Ward to transfer Joyce to a specially prepared room. McEntee is an infectious diseases ward, but because there was no room available in the amputees' ward, special arrangements had to be made for Joyce at the McEntee Ward. To the

Glory of God and the dedicated service of the medical and para-medical services of the hospital, Joyce began to make slow and steady progress. Physiotherapy was a major aspect of her recovery programme. She had to undertake daily exercises to strengthen her muscles. In order to have the energy to undertake these exercises, she needed to eat nutritious food, and this meant being put on a structured, strictly monitored eating plan. Her feeding programme started with liquids, before she moved on to eating soft food, and then to normal food. In the beginning, Joyce had to be fed by a nurse. When she became strong enough to feed herself, she had to be taught to eat with specially adapted cutlery, because she had limited use of her hands, having lost seven of her fingers. It was a happy moment for Joyce when she was able to eat her favourite Nigerian food again, particularly when it was made by Sister Toyin, as opposed to the "just tolerable" food prepared by me!

By then, Joyce had spent three months in the McEntee Ward, and four months in the intensive care unit, making a total of seven months at St George's Hospital. Sepsis had done its worst, without succeeding in taking Joyce's life. The next step was a transfer to the specialist rehabilitation centre for amputees at Queen Mary's Hospital, Roehampton, which is run by St George's Hospital Trust. Queen Mary's Hospital is one of the world's leading amputee rehabilitation centres. From the day her legs were amputated, Joyce had always believed, and dreamt, that one day she would be able to walk again. Now she was on her way to a place that would help her do it.

Joyce was making good progress with her rehabilitation. Her stumps and hands needed daily dressing, she was having speech therapy for her stammering, and undergoing training to enable her to become gradually independent after her discharge from the hospital. However, she still had to learn how to move from a bed into a wheelchair and vice versa, how to use disabled bathroom facilities (with a carer's help where necessary), how to look after her personal hygiene, and how to manage cooking in the kitchen again, with adapted equipment where possible. I had to be involved with the training for many of these things, since I would have to be her main carer when she returned home. It was particularly important for me to learn how to use a transfer board. Otherwise known as banana board, this is used to transfer a disabled person from a wheelchair into a car and vice versa.

After nine weeks at Queen Mary's Hospital and its amputee rehabilitation centre, famously known as the Douglas Bader Unit, it was decided that Joyce was well enough to be discharged and to go home. But first, Joyce's OT (occupational therapist), a lovely lady named Melissa Jacobs, had to come and carry out an assessment of the house to see what facilities needed to be provided. We live in a semi-detached three-bedroom house, with one bathroom upstairs and a guest toilet off the hallway leading to the lounge downstairs. The entrance doorway is some six inches high, so we were going to need a ramp to enable Joyce's wheelchair to enter and exit the house. A mobile ramp could be provided, pending the building of a permanent ramp. However, Joyce could not access the bedrooms and bathroom, which are all upstairs. That presented several challenges. It would've been too risky to provide her with a stair lift, because most of her fingers had been amputated, and control of the stairlift chair would be difficult. A vertical lift through the ceiling to the master bedroom was considered, but it would have taken so much space – a single bed would hardly fit into the room, with little space left for wheelchair movement. The conclusion was that the long-term solution was to build an extension bedroom with bathroom facilities at the back of the house.

Meanwhile, Joyce was to be provided with a single adjustable hospital care bed placed in the lounge, a bedside commode for night use, and a transit wheelchair. The guest toilet was very small, and manoeuvring even a small wheelchair in and out would be quite challenging. Despite these challenges, the desire to go home in time for Christmas after a long and traumatic hospitalisation was overwhelming. And so, Joyce was discharged and came home on December 17th, 2015, over nine months since she had descended into the dark hole of unconsciousness. "To God be the glory, great things He hath done." Great was our rejoicing at her homecoming, and greater still our wonder that the Lord had answered our prayers. Praise the Lord! Praise the Lord!

Now began the task of looking after Joyce at home. There were hospital outpatient appointments and clinics to attend. I had to transport Joyce in my car, transferring her from the transit wheelchair with the banana board, so-called because of its shape, then pushing her in the wheelchair to the various appointments or for shopping in the stores. For someone who had been cooped up in hospital for over nine months, these outings, imbued with the sights and sounds of the outside world, were probably more recuperative, rejuvenating, and relaxing for Joyce than any medicine.

As I've mentioned, the guest toilet in our house is extremely small. Therefore, navigating this room for Joyce was quite challenging. It was impossible for her to shower in this room, because of the restricted size. A wash could be managed, but not a shower. So, we had to go all the way to Queen Mary's Hospital in Roehampton for me to give Joyce a bath, usually every Friday. Even the process of getting that done was sometimes tricky, if not a little embarrassing. The ladies' bathroom facilities are located next to the gymnasium. Because Joyce needed my help with showering, we had to negotiate our way through the ladies' facilities using a town crier technique to announce to the ladies that a male needed to come into their territory. Seeing Joyce's condition, the women usually showed understanding. Sometimes there would be one person who would raise a disapproving, perhaps just quizzical, eyebrow. However, with the kind cooperation of the Queen Mary's Hospital Rehabilitation Centre, Joyce continued to use the bathroom facilities in Roehampton until our house extension was completed in June 2018.

Getting the one-bedroom house extension done was another major challenge which was eventually overcome to the glory of God. As soon as Joyce returned home from the hospital in December 2015, we applied to Merton Council for a grant to build the extension. The plan was to remove the conservatory at the back of the house and build a one-bedroom extension to include shower and toilet facilities for the disabled. The maximum grant for a house extension project is set at £30,000, which includes all professional services costs, fees, and value-added tax. The grant was approved, but only after a long bureaucratic process. The council then appointed their consultants to design the building, produce cost estimates, process and select contractors, and supervise the project to completion. The estimated cost of the project came to about £56,000. Before the council would approve commencement of the project, we were required to show evidence of funds to cover the balance of £26,000. Here again, God sent help from above, through friends who organised a GoFundMe to supplement funds from the Council. The actual construction did not start until October 2016, and it was finally delivered in June 2018.

Between December 2015 and June 2018, we continued to receive and witness the grace of God. For me, the most amazing grace was the strength God provided me with to bear the physical, psychological, and mental burden of Joyce's debilitating illness and disability. When she came back from the hospital and had to sleep in the lounge on a single bed, I spent the night on a sofa close to her bed.

However, after some time, Joyce saw how uncomfortable and tiring it was for me to do this. She persuaded me to go back to sleeping in our room upstairs, and she would call me whenever she needed help, usually only when she needed to use the toilet. Otherwise she was able to get on the commode herself, and I would empty and clean the potty in the morning. When she was able to employ carers later, I was relieved of some of the burden, at least during the day. But it was difficult to find carers willing to do other housework in addition to Joyce's personal care. I had to do a lot of ironing, particularly of Tolu's clothes, which naturally were always a handful. But I was always encouraged by Apostle Paul's message to the Philippians: "I can do all things through Christ who strengthens me."

One thing that Joyce was determined to start doing as soon as possible, was cooking for the family. Once pushed into the kitchen in her wheelchair, she was able to turn her disability into ability through adaptability. Her willpower is amazing. She found a way to overcome many difficulties in order to become as independent as possible. She scoured the internet daily to search for gadgets to help her in the consuming quest, and was not afraid to try anything.

For Joyce, real freedom came when she got an electric wheelchair. For the first time, nobody needed to be pushing her around (no pun intended!) in the transit wheelchair. She was as free as a bird. And did she fly! She could go on the buses on her own, and do all her shopping in her own time, at her own pace. When we got the mobility vehicle, she could come aboard in her wheelchair, and I could drive her wherever we or she needed to go. And if I was not available to take her in the vehicle, off she went on her own. She is a profile in courage. As Chief Obafemi Awolowo, the legendary Nigerian statesman, famously said, "It is not life that matters, but the courage you bring into it." Joyce obviously takes to heart the admonition of Apostle Matthew in his Gospel (10:28) – "Do not be afraid of those who kill the body but cannot kill the soul. Rather be afraid of the One who can destroy both soul and body in hell."

Chapter 6 –

Family and Friends

In this chapter, my family and friends have written their own pieces on how they reacted when they heard of my illness, how they coped, and their encouragement towards me.

MY SON – ORE

I can remember pretty well everything that happened to Mum. I was in the library at the University of Birmingham, when I got a text from her that she was feeling ill and had driven herself to the hospital. I asked if she was okay, and she said she would be fine. She also asked me when I was coming home, and I said I would be home in a few days, as the Easter holidays had come up. When I arrived back in London, Mum wasn't home, which was strange – as I had assumed she would've been back from the hospital, only to find out from my father that she had extended her stay. I was immediately worried.

So, I rushed to St George's Hospital. Mum was in a ward, awake, with all her belongings beside her. The doctors came in and out to do tests, and they spoke in such confusing terms that I didn't really understand what they were saying. It later came to my knowledge that they had no clue as to what was wrong with her. When I spoke to my mum, she was soft-spoken and tired. She asked me how school was, and she told me that there was nothing to worry about it, and that she would be home for Easter. Mum also said something else to me that I have never been able to forget: no matter what happened, I shouldn't drop out of school, but to finish, as I was in my last year.

She had said this because I had figured out that this illness was worse than it seemed, and told her that I would drop out or take a year out if necessary. She flatly refused. I went home and my spirit was troubled. My appetite was lost, and my energy was depleted.

Not long after, Mum fell into a coma. When I say not long, I mean the same day. Dad was the first to get the news, and he came home to tell me. At the time, I was taking care of my sister, Tolu. Dad waited until Tolu was asleep before he broke the news to me. I was shocked, and couldn't believe what I was hearing. I felt like someone had taken the bottom half of my body from under me. I couldn't feel my legs, and all I did was stare back at him. Furthermore, he told me that the doctors had given Mum twenty-four hours to live. There was a sudden burst of heat in my chest, and I could hear the sound of my own breathing. I have never felt a sensation like that in my entire life. I asked him, 'What did you say?' and he said to me – with such boldness – that the doctors were wrong and that God would pull Mum through. He told me that, 16 years ago, he had been through a similar experience. Yet still, he did not fear, because he had put his faith in God. 'I prostrate before you, Lord, flat on the ground,' he said. Despite his words filling me with confidence, I began to tremble, out of fear for my mother and the sense of abrupt change that had suddenly taken my family. Dad left before we could discuss anything further, to go back to the hospital to stay with my mum, whilst I stayed at home to look after my sister, Tolu, the little angel. My walk up the stairs to my room was heavy and burdened. I've never had death fill my thoughts so quickly and at such a pace. I believed. I had faith. But in my mind's eye, I was scared that the shadow of death was upon my mum, and I was terrified. I prayed and then slept. Then prayed, then slept. I repeated this for several hours throughout the night.

Around 6 a.m. I heard the door open. I jumped out of bed and headed to the top of the stairs. Dad came through and saw me. He said three words to me: 'She made it.' My heart pounded so fast that I had no choice but to hold my chest. Mum was still in a coma, but she was better than the night before. I started to thank God so much. I was able to lift my head with a full heart and push on.

When I got to the hospital to see Mum, she was much better. Asleep, yes, but much better. The machines were still on and connected to her body. During that entire period, different things were happening. My dad became incredibly paranoid. He didn't want anybody near my mum or seeing her, except family. So, whenever friends from church came to see her, and they said they were my mum's "sisters" the nurses grew suspicious. It turned out my mum had at least ten sisters and counting. All that stopped immediately, and the nurses had to have a list of the people allowed to be near her. Maybe my father started to believe that this sickness was spiritual, beyond human understanding. Maybe this was some sort of spiritual warfare that he had only just become aware of. It was too hard to tell. Even I got cautious. I didn't want to talk too much to people I didn't know, and I certainly was not allowing anyone to come with me inside the ward. I was there so often that some nurses knew me by name. The canteen food became familiar; the nurses' scrubs became the usual uniform I would see. But the doctors were different. Different sets of doctors would crowd round Mum every time I came, as if she was a lab experiment, as if they were showing wonders. And I guess, as doctors, maybe that is how they saw it. The fact that she was alive after their prediction stunned them. Young and old doctors came along holding clipboards, taking notes, talking across her, checking her blood, and then moving on. It was like science class was in session, and they were having practicals.

Throughout that period, I was in the hospital almost every day – afternoon and evening – consistently without fail. I didn't have the energy or strength to revise or go over any work for my exams. My Aunty Toyin arrived from Nigeria not long after. There was tension in the house, and that created a very strained atmosphere. The tense situation at home was unbearable for me in addition to the existing pain of my mother's illness. Besides, my father and I could take care of ourselves and my sister; at least that's what I thought. Soon my father's sister (Mrs. Bode Akande) made meals for us to eat. She prepared various dishes for us throughout the nine months while my mum was in the hospital. She continued to cook food for us even after Mum was discharged home from hospital, until Mum was able to do the cooking herself. I was so grateful for this;

her heart is so big and the memory makes me smile.

When my Aunt Toyin arrived, she made her intentions clear – she was here to support my mother and provide emotional support. My uncle also came along and visited my mother in the hospital, and it was good for Mum to be surrounded by family at such a tough time. Throughout this time, my sister had no real idea what was happening. Being so young, it was better that she was shielded from all the trauma. My dad made sure that Tolu's routine was the same and nothing changed, but Aunty Toyin's influence started to rub off. Soon my sister was dressing herself and cleaning up and doing things she never did before, which was good.

I, on the other hand, was trying to navigate out of my emotional wilderness. I didn't know what to feel, how to react, what to think or say. I walked around my church a number of times, hoping for a sign, hoping for something that could give me clarity. I just couldn't get my head around it. What was the point? What was the lesson in this experience? What did we do wrong? Did I do something wrong that my mum was paying for? I didn't get it. My mistake was that I tried to anticipate the effect this experience would have on me. The truth is, it almost destroyed me emotionally. I thought courage was the ability to withstand pain, to endure, to suffer in silence, and to put on a brave face. That was my error of judgement. It is the complete opposite. Unfortunately, it took me a while to understand and accept this, and during that time I was overwhelmed with such an unforgettable level of sadness, that anybody that showed me a modicum of kindness only took me further into a place of despair, where I couldn't even recognise who I was anymore. Maybe it was depression.

Still, my exams were around the corner and I had to make a big judgement call. As mentioned, Mum had told me to stay in school no matter what. So, I did just that. I went back to university and studied for my exams. At the same time, I went to see my mother at the hospital. A week and a bit had passed before I had last seen her. I made my way to the ward where my mother was. She was no longer in a coma, but when I came she was asleep. I recall seeing her legs for the first time. They were black as night, with a few light patches. The soles of her feet were still as normal, but the colour contrast was strange. She was still connected to a machine, and there was a slender tube tipped with a needle in her veins.

When I came in closer, she opened her eyes. I said, 'Mum,' and she just blinked. I realised she was mute and couldn't speak. She smiled a little, so I just took the initiative and started talking and saying the things I knew she would have asked.

'I'm okay, school is fine. I haven't started any exams, my friends send their prayers.' She raised her eyebrows. She became relaxed, all this communicated through her facial expressions. I guess it could be said that I know her expressions really well, so whenever she looked at me, I reassured her that I had eaten, I was okay, and that I was just checking in on her. I remember looking around and seeing pictures of me, my dad, and my sister on a side table. There was also a table there, with a radio on it. I put it on and played Magic FM for a little while, but Mum got tired of it very quickly. I asked if she had eaten, and if she was alright. She nodded. I then told her I was going, kissed her forehead, and left.

After I left, I went to a Chinese restaurant, bought some food, and sat on a bench. I ate and I thought. There wasn't much else to do. My exams were not too far away, my mother was in the hospital, my mind was a mess. Yet again, I kept telling myself to be tough, which in my world means to not show that you are in pain. I was numb to it all. I was too busy trying to make sense of things. Even when my exams began, I tried to take my mind off things. My friends tried distracting me, but it was tough. There was one occasion where I was in the cinema, and I had a missed call from my father. I panicked. I called back, and he said it was a mistake. I was livid. My heart had been racing, not knowing what that missed call meant.

When my exams finished, I made my way back home and then I went back to the hospital. There, I found out that things had been happening, and that there was progress on my mum's condition. First, I was told that whilst I was away at university, she could have died at any time. I wasn't given this information due to the sensitivity and the time, but even now I still wish I had known. At this time my birthday was coming up, and I just wanted to celebrate in peace and think about life. I remembered something my aunt had said to me at one point when I stayed with her in Nigeria, when I was much younger. I was waking up late, not cleaning up after myself or tidying my surroundings, when she said to me, 'What will you do when you are on your own? What will you do?' Now, those words rang in my ears – to the point where it was deafening. Now I had to think about those words seriously – what would I actually do? It was like God had put a shield around the earth, and my prayers fell back at the speed of a shooting star – unanswered. What could possibly happen? What else was in store for me? Maybe I had hurt someone in another life, and this was retribution. A few days after my birthday, I was told my mum would be having her legs and fingers amputated, and that she had already given the go ahead without saying anything to me or my dad.

The journey to the hospital was the longest journey I had ever made in my life. It's a 15-minute journey by car, and my father was driving. It felt like a lifetime. When we got there, the limbs were already gone. Mum couldn't talk, because she was still under anaesthesia. There I was, looking at the space where her legs had been. The surgeons had gotten rid of the legs and the fingers they amputated. At that moment, a wave of disillusionment came down on me so hard that I couldn't lift my shoulders. I felt as if God wasn't really interested in me anymore. I never asked to be rich, or for fame and glory, or to have lots of nice things, so what was the point? What was the essence? What do you want from me? I felt like God had betrayed me in some sense. My trust was in Him, and now it felt like it was worthless. If only the ground would open up and swallow me! Put me in a desert, let me remain there, rather than to go through this process of recycled pain over and over again. My heart was shattered, and I felt as though someone had taken a sledgehammer and made an attempt to crush my spirit and my soul. No legs? No fingers? What else did God want to take? I wish he didn't ask me to trust Him in the midst of all this.

When we got home, the house was quiet. At that moment, unbeknown to me, depression had kicked in – self-diagnosed of course. Later, Mum began suffering from delirium, seeing things that were not there, and recanting things from decades ago. 'Oh, they haven't bathed me in weeks,' she would say. I would ask the nurses, only for them to say they had given her a bath a day ago. That was when I realised the depth of this. 'God!' I exclaimed. At this point I thought we had crossed the Rubicon. It would be wicked and cruel of me to say, 'Why her and not anybody else?' because that would mean someone else deserved it instead of her, when God loves all equally. I became so cautious of anything good that came my way, because I was so afraid that it would be taken away from me without question, without thought, without consideration, and without option, and certainly without choice. The only question left was, 'Who's next?' or better yet, 'Whose turn?'

God hadn't finished with us, He was just getting started. Thankfully, the nurses and doctors confirmed that delirium was just a symptom and one of the after effects of amputations. It lasted a few days. Not long after this, my mother was moved to another ward due to her progress and recovery from delirium. I remember walking into the ward she was in before, and I saw an empty bed. I panicked, until I was informed that she had been moved. However, something had changed. Her spirit had been affected, naturally of course, and she needed people to talk to now more than ever. I remember the hospital chaplain coming in and out of Mum's ward room a few times. I knew why he was there, but I had no idea of the content of their conversations, so I pressed her to tell me. Mum said she felt guilty, because she wanted to die – that's how bad the pain was. She thought such thoughts were sinful. The chaplain wasn't there to absolve her, but he was there to let her know that it was okay, and that he was available if she wanted to talk.

A chance encounter had a sustained impact on my perspective. I was on the way to the hospital, when I bumped into an old acquaintance, and she asked me where I was going. When I told her that I was going to St George's, she said that she didn't like that hospital, because her mother had died of cancer. She told me to be strong, and to be grateful to God that my mother was still alive, still communicating, and still able to do things.

When she said all this, I took a moment to ponder – to think. Had I been ungrateful, selfish even? I also found myself circling my church, hoping God would just give me a sign that He was present, that He had us in mind. Maybe the friend I bumped into was the only sign I needed. All Mum needed was for someone to understand and get her perspective. It was tough for me to take, because it gave me an insight into her pain and emotions. I couldn't find the words to comfort her, so all I did was listen instead when it was my turn to spend time with my mum. Every day I would come in to see her, talk to her, laugh whenever we could. But it was tough, because I just couldn't get my head around it all. As the months passed, she started to improve, eating a lot more, talking a lot more, smiling, laughing, and having a more positive outlook on life.

Seven months later, she was moved to Queen Mary's Hospital in Roehampton, and this was where her rehabilitation would start. On the one hand, I was happy that she would begin her journey towards full recovery, and on the other hand, I was experiencing a deep sadness that I couldn't explain. I finally realised that I was having difficulty getting over everything. Meanwhile, my mother had kept her eyes on the prize: to get her strength back and to pursue the idea of not only being independent, but of maybe walking again one day.

Every time I made the bus journey to the hospital, I always wondered what that day would bring. What could possibly happen this time? Thankfully, all I witnessed was my mother going from strength to strength. She had been watching motivational videos on YouTube, she was becoming a lot more positive, and, more importantly, growing closer to God. As far as she was concerned, happiness was a decision, and she decided every day when she woke up that she was going to be happy and thank God for his blessings. Before her workout, it would be prayer and meditation. Then some exercises and gym work, and then back to bed. My mum is tough and incredibly resilient. After a few months at Queen Mary's, she was making good progress, and she even came home for a few days. I guess seeing her smile and watching her laugh made me happy in some way. I loved going to the market and getting her food, whether it was Chinese (her favourite) or some jollof rice from one of the Nigerian stalls in the market. I would make sure the bowls were packed with all the bits that she liked. That being said, it was tough to get over it all emotionally. I needed counselling and a lot of time to assess the effects on my own mental health and well-being. But one thing I recognised is that my mother is tough, strong, resilient, and has a heart full of faith and hope. That was all she needed, and frankly it was more than enough to lead her on a road to recovery.

Oreoluwa

TOSIN OTUN – MY NIECE

Joyce is my aunt – my mother's younger sister – and we have a very close bond. I spent my growing years living with Joyce, and have learnt so much from her. We had fun trips travelling, but what we enjoyed most was shopping for skincare products together at Selfridge's department store in London, and there was always some pampering facial to enjoy too. We would ride the bus to Oxford Street from South West London chatting all the way whatever the weather; a quick stop at Harrods to pick her favourite cocoa-dusted almonds followed by lunch at Leicester Square. It had become our aunt-niece tradition. Joyce has always been a pillar of support and my go-to person for advice, who showed me that everything and anything is possible.

I remember the day that everything changed very clearly. It was 3.30 p.m. Easter Sunday, 2015, and I had called my aunt's phone several times to wish her happy Easter; it was most unlike her not to have returned my calls. Eventually, around 5 p.m. she called back. She was at A&E (Accident and Emergency), St George's Hospital.

I remember her account: 'I haven't been feeling well, went to the doctor's office and was asked to take some tests, nothing came back odd, but I know there is something wrong. I just know there is something not quite right.'

Having spent my growing years around my aunt, I can easily tell when it's just panic on her mind. This time, however, I could not figure it out; she sounded okay, but odd. Maybe she just had a moment of pain, I kept thinking, but I was hoping it was nothing serious. Whatever it was, I was not taking it lightly. Not long after, a call came through from my mother. I could hear the panic in her voice when she asked, 'Joyce is in A&E; do you know exactly why she is there?' But I am used to my mother, who would panic at every piece of news – even a slight headache – so I gave her my reassurance that all was well.

Auntie Joyce called again around 6.30 p.m. She was still at A&E, and she wanted me to pass on an urgent message because she could not reach the person. This time, I could sense she was breathing heavily because, though her words were clear, she had to pause between her words. She now had an oxygen mask on. At that moment, I felt the fear grip me. A million questions flooded my mind, uncertainties building, and at that moment I said a short prayer. I must confess that I was scared for what was to follow.

I was awakened a little after midnight by the sound of an incoming text message. It was my uncle, Auntie Joyce's husband, saying that Auntie Joyce was now in a coma and that we should pray. Time stood still. Goosebumps suddenly covered my body, and I remember screaming so loudly that it woke my husband from sleep. He tried to calm me, because I was crying inconsolably. I was so confused. We had only been talking on the phone barely five hours earlier. What could have happened? I tried to pray, but it was the shortest prayer in my entire existence, because my mind was far away in London. If only I could see Joyce, talk to her, pray into her ears, and beg her not to go. I thought of my cousins, and of Tolu, her seven-year-old daughter, my cousin Ore and uncle; so many thoughts flashed through my mind in a millisecond. I was deeply distressed.

My first reaction was to call my mother to inform her of my aunt's condition, but she was alone at home. It was 1 a.m., and I wasn't sure how she was going to react. I was in no frame of mind to console her, so my best bet was to call my brother and ask him to call Mum. As I spoke to my brother, I could tell he also was saddened by this adverse turn of events; we needed to make all the arrangements for one of us to get to London by the very next day.

I had now been awake for five hours. My husband kept encouraging me with Bible verses. He prayed, and specifically reminded me about the very thing we know my aunt for: she is strong and she is a fighter; she would surely pull through. Yet, as daylight broke, we received bad news – the doctors said that Joyce had only 24 hours to live. It was a holiday in Nigeria and in London. I called my friends and my pastor to join my family in prayers for my aunt.

I made up my mind to fight for her. Throughout the day, I prayed like I had never done before, because I wanted her back.

> James 5: 14:
>
> *"Is any sick among you? Let him call for the elders of the church; and let them pray over him, anointing him with oil in the name of the Lord."*

24 hours passed, and Joyce was still in a coma, but contrary to doctors' reports, she was alive! What an awesome God we serve. What was meant to shake my faith, instead strengthened it. I knew that if she could have gone beyond 24 hours, she would pull through for more than 24 days, weeks, months, and years! We continued earnestly in prayers; I called my mum in London every day for the next few weeks, and daily she would say, 'Let us continue to pray.' Waiting to see my aunt regain consciousness was a challenging time for my family. With Joyce still in a coma, and with organ failure and amputation, I relied on scriptures – specifically the Psalms – for daily encouragement. I was convinced that my aunt would get better, but I did not know when this was going to be. So, I meditated on the scriptures, and prayed with friends and family:

> Malachi 3:6:
>
> *"For I, the LORD, do not change; therefore you, O sons of Jacob, are not consumed."*

> Hebrews 13:8:
>
> *"Jesus Christ is the same yesterday, today and forever."*

Psalm 18: 6:

"In my distress I called to the Lord; I cried to my God for help. From his temple he heard my voice; my cry came before him, into his ears."

On the first day that Joyce showed signs of consciousness, it felt like I had just crossed the finish line and won first place in the Olympic 1500 meter race. I jumped, cried, sang praises to God, and laughed. It was a mix of emotions, but it was pure joy – like I had never felt before. She had won the battle again. God had given her the victory, because He promised He would never leave us nor forsake us.

Isaiah 43:2:

"Do not fear, for I have redeemed you; I have summoned you by name; you are mine. When you pass through the waters, I will be with you; and when you pass through the rivers, they will not sweep over you. When you walk through the fire, you will not be burned; the flames will not set you ablaze. For I am the Lord your God, the Holy One of Israel, your Savior."

The excitement of seeing my aunt alive at the hospital brought tears of joy. It was July 2015, and she had been in the hospital for four months. These were long summer days, and I looked forward to my evening visits at the hospital. Joyce got better, and stronger, and is so much stronger today too. God has been so good to us. I will never forget our Christmas celebrations in 2016, as my aunt and I – with our families – spent time together; it was the best time in that year. She has been my daily source of inspiration as she returns to her regular activities, both at home and outside the home. She fearlessly tackles every task and achieves her goals. She sees no limitations and she has no regrets. She reminds me daily of the following:

I am eternally grateful to God for all that He has done. I know the Lord shall continue to strengthen my aunt, body, soul, and spirit. God is faithful, and He continues to show His grace in our lives. I look forward to us getting back to our aunt-niece traditions soon. I stand on the word of God.

Tosin Otun

PROFESSOR LADIPO OTOLORIN – MY COUSIN

"If you're believing in God for a medical miracle, always remember, doctors only practice and God performs."

- Diva Fierce

The story of what happened to my cousin, Mrs. Joyce Oluwole, was both a miracle and a medical feat. When she asked me to write a few lines on how I handled the news about her illness, that request brought many frightful memories to my mind. My initial reaction was to remind her that I am a very busy person, and should have been given more than five days to do justice to the topic. However, on second thought, I decided to put down a few words, during a four-hour train ride from Ellicott City to Bridgeport Station in the USA.

Let me first introduce myself, and explain the relationship between me and Joyce. My name is Prof. Emmanuel Oladipo Otolorin, the first son of the late Dr. Michael Price Otolorin, who was the elder brother of Joyce's father, the late Dr. Timothy R. Adeola Otolorin. Joyce is my cousin. When my father died about 11 years ago, I became the *Oloriebi* (i.e., head) of my father's nuclear family. My cousin, Toyin Otolorin, who is older than I am, is truly the Oloriebi of the entire Otolorin family of Abeokuta, Ogun State of Nigeria.

A few years ago, I received a telephone call from Toyin to say that her junior sister Joyce was very ill and had been admitted to a hospital in London. She asked that we should all join her in prayers for a successful recovery. At that time, I had no knowledge of the extent of Joyce's illness, other than that she had some kind of infection. I then relayed the information to my siblings through our social media forum, and asked for special prayers for Joyce to overcome this challenge. A few days later, I called Toyin to find out about her sister's progress, only to be informed that Joyce had slipped into a coma and was having difficulty breathing. Furthermore, her limb extremities were changing colour. That raised alarm bells in me. As a medical practitioner, my mind immediately went to a generalised infectious process, probably leading to septicaemia and possible multiple organ failure. However, knowing that she was in the United Kingdom, where I did my postgraduate education in Obstetrics and Gynaecology, I felt that she was probably in the best hands to manage such a complicated case. I knew that such specialist hospitals had the wherewithal to support failed organs during treatment. Had she been in Nigeria at the time of her illness, perhaps the story would have been different today.

To calm my cousin Toyin down, I told her about a few real-life examples that I was aware of. In one such case, the patient had been diagnosed with generalized septicaemia, complicated by multiple organ failure. As part of her treatment, she was put into a medically induced coma to allow for specialist management of the condition. In both instances, thankfully, the outcomes were good. Remembering these cases gave me a ray of hope, and I started praying for the doctors and support staff who were managing Joyce to do the right thing. I suspected that the bugs causing the infection were probably hospital-acquired multidrug resistant strains, that would require special antibiotics to kill them. Therefore, my siblings and I prayed that God would look favourably on our cousin, and allow all the medications to work. I was certainly not under any illusion about the fact that while "doctors care for patients, only God heals." In my professional career, I have seen so many instances of so-called hopeless cases that the Almighty God pulled back from the brink of death, and so I joined others to pray that Joyce would be one such success story.

One thing I could not, however, get out of my mind was the information that Joyce's limb extremities were turning black. To me that meant that gangrene was setting in, and that something radical would have to be done soon to stop the ascent of this horrible complication. Hence, I kept calling my cousin to get updates on the status of Joyce's toes and fingers, but the feedback was not very good. I was therefore not too surprised when Toyin, my cousin, called to say that the doctors had taken the decision to carry out amputations of the most affected parts of Joyce's limbs in order to save her life. That made medical sense to me, as I would rather have a cousin with a disability than to hear that she died. I did feel a little bit of compassion for whoever had to give consent on behalf of comatose Joyce for the surgery to be done. I knew that whoever gave that consent would have been concerned about what to tell Joyce whenever she woke up. Thankfully, this matter was later handled professionally, and Joyce has since emerged to be a very strong woman who is also very thankful to God to be alive today.

So, what lessons did I learn from this experience? Firstly, this case has once again demonstrated to me the awesomeness of God in our lives. As someone named Emmanuel (God with Us), I have never doubted His presence to intervene whenever our earthly brains fail to find solutions to complex situations. From day to day, He continues to reveal himself to us through new medical research findings that are advancing health care delivery globally. Thankfully, my cousin was one of the beneficiaries of these advances in medical practice.

The second lesson I learnt, was in understanding the difference between health care delivery in the developed and developing countries. The level of preparedness of hospitals in the developed countries to manage life-threatening complications is simply awesome. Availability of specially trained and highly motivated personnel, functional support laboratories, availability of medications and life-saving commodities, functional equipment, and consumable supplies supported by appropriate logistic management information systems, have laid the foundation for optimum patient care. Visionary leadership, and adequate healthcare financing, knit all these together. In contrast, many hospitals in the developing countries lack most of the above. Low supplies of life-saving medications, consumable supplies, and test kits, shortage of human resources for health, outdated and non-functional equipment, are commonplace in these facilities. To compound the challenges, political and institutional leadership have often been short-sighted and have failed to prioritise health care delivery.

In closing, I wish to thank the Almighty God in sparing the life of our cousin, and pray that He will grant her long life, much better health, and prosperity. Obviously, God spared Joyce's life for a reason. May she discover that reason and be strengthened to fulfil it in Jesus's Mighty Name, Amen.

MY OLDER SISTER – TOYIN

HIS DIVINE FAVOUR AND FAITHFULNESS

1. "Before they call I will answer; while they are still speaking I will hear." – Isaiah 65 verse 24. "Whatever you ask for in my name I will do. I will lift up my eyes to the hills, from whence comes my help." – (Psalm 121 verse 1).

2. "Howbeit this kind goeth not out but by prayer and fasting?" – (Matthew 17 verse 21).

3. "Not by might, nor by power, but by my spirit, saith the LORD of hosts." – (Zechariah 4 verse 6).

4. "That they may know you, the only TRUE GOD and JESUS CHRIST whom you have sent." – (John 17 verse 13). "The Apostle Paul added; 'That I may know Him and the power of HIS resurrection'." – (Philippians 3 verse 10).

5. "The thief does not come except to steal and to kill and to destroy. I have come that they may have life and that they may have it more abundantly." – (John 10 verse 10).

6. "My people perish for lack of enough knowledge." – (Hosea 4 verse 6).

7. "Go therefore and preach the good news and make disciples of all nations." – (Matthew 28 verse 19).

8. "I will not die but live to declare the Glory of GOD." – (Psalm 118 verse 17).

When I heard the bad news about my sister's predicament, I was devastated, lost, helpless, anxious, and weepy. I decided to go into fervent prayer and fasting for God's intervention, divine favour, and solution to the problem. I then went straight to London, to be by Joyce's side in the hospital, and stand in for her at home.

My perception of God's intervention in my sister's life is summed up in the insight and the Bible passages on the previous page. What the Lord has done for us as a family, especially for my sister Joyce, I cannot completely describe, but it is worth documenting.

Through Joyce's episode, God revealed and proved Himself in diverse dimensions. He revealed Himself as the miracle worker, prayer-answering God, the help of the helpless, hope of the hopeless, all-knowing, powerful, faithful, loving, and caring Father; as the Resurrection and life, the creator of the Universe, the forgiver of sins, the constant and covenant-keeping God; the healer, the greatest Physician. The I am that I am, as Jehovah Jireh, Jehovah Rapha, Jehovah Shalom, Jehovah Nissi, Jehovah El-Shaddai; the beginning and the end. Who then is like unto Him, there is no God like Him!

JESUS IS THE RESURRECTION AND THE LIFE – THE MIRACLE WORKER

For two months, Joyce was in a coma. She was diagnosed as having multiple organ failure, and her condition was resistant to several medications. All her organ systems shut down, and she depended on life-support equipment. Her body was degenerating, short of decomposing. This led to bilateral amputation of the two lower limbs and seven fingers. She had neither physical nor spiritual life. Even the medical team gave up hope of her coming back to life, but her husband and I hung on to the supernatural power of resurrection. At the end of two months, Jesus Christ proved Himself. Christ resurrected her and restored her to life! That's God the Almighty for you!

JESUS CHRIST AS THE ALL-KNOWING, POWERFUL, CARING, AND COVENANT-KEEPING GOD

Though my sister walked through the valley of the shadow of death, God's presence was evident. His rod and staff comforted her, as He arrested the rate of degeneration and decomposition. Whilst Joyce was passing through the fire and water (Isaiah 43 verse 2), the Lord brought to bear His promises.

"Fear not for I am with you, be not dismayed for am your God, I will strengthen you, yes, I will help you." – (Isaiah 41 verse 10).

"I will uphold you with my right hand. This is all about Jesus' assurance and timely intervention in all our challenges of life. If God is for us, who can be against us?" – (Romans 8 verse 31).

"No weapon fashioned against us shall ever prosper." – (Isaiah 54:17).

JESUS AS A GOOD SHEPHERD

Jesus the good shepherd gives quality and satisfying life, and this includes healing, salvation, provision, nourishment, and eternal life. All these, Jesus gives in abundance, in various ways. On the other hand, the devil (the thief), the bad shepherd, including his cohorts, takes life and replaces it with death. The bad shepherd is self-centred, and has no good intentions for his sheep.

Unfortunately, many people do not know the nature of this true shepherd (God) nor are they interested in serving Him. People are therefore held in bondage for their lack of knowledge of God. When we have a good knowledge of the truth (Our Lord Jesus Christ), the truth sets us free.

JESUS AS A LOVING AND CARING AND ETERNALLY LIVING GOD

God's deep love for mankind (including Joyce, you, and me) is evident in His offering His son as a sacrifice for us, so that we may receive forgiveness for our sins and live a satisfying and quality life. By God's grace, my sister does all things through Christ, who strengthens her. She is independent in activities of daily living, including self-care, mobility, domestic chores, work, and productivity. Her mental faculties and cognition are intact. So, therefore, because Jesus lives, Joyce is able to face tomorrow. All her fear is gone, because she knows that Christ holds the future; her life is worth living just because Jesus lives!

Jesus Christ in His love promises that He will never fail us nor leave us until the end of age. Even if we die, Christ will raise us up at the last day, so that we may live a more glorious life with Him in Eternity. This is the nature of our covenant-keeping God.

My sister's book also addresses the great commission of our Lord Jesus Christ as she publishes and circulates the GOOD news. Blessed are those who believe in God's word, and those who believe in His son Jesus Christ as our Saviour and Redeemer and the Reflection of our Heavenly father.

And so to God be the Glory, Great things He has done. Oh God, we are very grateful for all You have done for us as a family.

Toyin Otolorin

MY BROTHER – FREDDIE

Joyce is my beloved sister. I learnt of her illness through her husband, known to me as Uncle Sola. He only told me that my sister was in St George's Hospital, but he didn't tell me exactly what was wrong with her. I visited her at the hospital, but she was still hale and hearty at that point in time. Unfortunately, the next time I went to visit her, she had been transferred to another ward. Now, she was in a coma, on life-support machines. I was so distraught by what I saw that I went back to my car and cried my eyes out in the car park, and other car owners came around to find out why I was in such a distressed state.

On my third visit to the hospital, I met a friend of Joyce's from another church – and she prayed for both me and Joyce there and then. At this point, I thought that was it – Joyce was on her last lap. Her toes and some of her fingers had changed colour, and the doctors' prognosis was extremely grim. Psychologically, I was so distressed that I cried when driving back home.

Following this, I went to my church. They knew me well there, because I've played musical instruments for them for 20 years. They saw my face, and immediately started to suspect that there was something wrong. I went straight to the head pastor and told him about what had happened. He tried to pacify me, and then he prayed for Joyce and for me. Unfortunately, I realised that all of this distress had severely impacted my ability to play my guitar. I couldn't do it without making mistakes, due to my inability to focus on anything other than my beloved sister's situation. So, I was forced to suspend this.

After the service, I decided to go to St George's Hospital to see Joyce again. I got an enormous shock when I arrived, when I saw that both her legs had been amputated, and some of her fingers too. I was so devastated that I started to question God as to why and what we had done to deserve this. This was how I felt at the time. All this time, Joyce was on a number of medical machines to help her breathing and vital organs. My elder sister arrived from Nigeria shortly after this, and we often met at the hospital to discuss the situation and pray.

When she came back to life, Joyce was transferred to another ward. Thanks be to God. Initially, she could not understand what had been happening, and that made me develop goosepimples with fright – but at least she could recognise me. She started getting better, and she could talk, but the tubes from the machines were still passing through her neck. Unfortunately, I wasn't getting better. There were times when I never went out even for fresh air. I stayed indoors for four to five days at a stretch. I was not eating properly, and I lost my appetite. The impact it had on me was shocking. I didn't know that I could do without food and drink for three to four days at a stretch due to worry, and yet I was not hungry or thirsty – just very physically weak.

When Joyce was given the green light to go home, I was relieved, and I thanked God for His mercies. I have tried getting over the shock, but it has been so very difficult and slow. It is a gradual process, and I am trying to move forward. I always stand in for Joyce in my church for special prayers, and that has helped me through. My health immunity has been low, but I am pulling through – in Jesus's name.

Freddie-Mills Otolorin

MY YOUNGER SISTER – FOLAKE

I first heard that Joyce was ill through my older sister. When she informed me that she had to go to the UK to check on Joyce, my initial reaction was of surprise. I had spoken to Joyce on the phone some days earlier and she sounded hale and hearty.

As the days turned into weeks, I became anxious, but my older sister would calm me down. She would remind me that God was in control and that everything would be alright. Then, one day, my sister told me Joyce had gone into a coma. I was absolutely shocked by this. My heart started racing at a thousand beats a minute (or so I thought). I was so scared! I immediately went into a session of non-stop midnight prayers and fasting. I prayed really hard that God should spare Joyce's life, bring her out of the coma, and return her to us.

On the 4th of July, 2015, I got a call. It was Tosin (my niece) on the line:

'Hello, Tosin. How is Joyce?'

'She's fine; she wants to speak with you,' she replied. I was ecstatic!

Then Joyce said to me, 'Fola, won ti ge ese mi.' *Fola, they have amputated my legs.*

I was stunned by this. 'What?! Why?' I asked.

'Ese mejeji,' Joyce said. *Both of them.*

I froze. For some seconds, I was speechless. Then, my brain readjusted, and I knew that what Joyce needed was words of encouragement, and a reminder of the need to stand with faith in God.

I said, 'Be strong, and hang in there. We don't want to lose you.'

In summary, what I have learnt from this experience is indeed that God is faithful and that "prayer changeth things". Joyce is a living miracle, a testimony of God's goodness to her and the entire family. With God, all things are possible.

I would like to express my gratitude to her husband, Uncle Sola, for his steadfastness, faithfulness, and undying love for Joyce. The Lord will surely reward him abundantly. Amen.

Mrs. Folake Somorin

MY FRIENDS

MY TWIN – DOTUN ADEMOLA

'In everything give thanks to our Almighty Father. I could have lost my life during the many surgeries. God must have kept me alive for a reason.' These were the words Joyce said to me over the phone, when she came out of her coma, and they have stayed with me ever since.

When my dear friend Teni called me that fine morning, I was not ready for what she was about to tell me. I was still struggling to accept the passing of my beloved sister and brother. I wanted no more bad news for a long time to come. In my country, if you are asked when the last time was that you heard from or saw someone, just know there is bad news!

So, when our friend asked me, 'When was the last time you heard from Joyce?', my answer was, 'I don't want to hear, I don't want to know.' Then the tears started rolling. She said, 'Joyce is alive, but her situation is bad.' I still did not want to hear it, but she told me anyway. I sobbed uncontrollably. She told me how miserable she had been when she heard, but felt better after speaking with Joyce – and encouraged me to do the same. Speak with Joyce? What was I expected to say to her? Not me! I was already overwhelmed with anger, guilt, and regret, having been out of touch for so long. I learnt a lesson: always stay in touch with loved ones, no matter what. Joyce and I met in high school 53 years ago, and became close enough to call each other twins. I was to be her chief bridesmaid, but couldn't make it for health reasons. We were that close!

A few days later, I received a fundraising video with Joyce's photograph on a hospital bed. I did not open it, and I did not call Joyce. I just could not bring myself to see her without her beautiful legs. I was aware that she knew I had heard, so I sent her a message. We reconnected by sending and receiving messages from each other, but no phone calls! I let other friends know by sending the fundraising video to them, but I still could not call Joyce.

Ultimately, a touching message from Joyce gave me the courage I needed. She wrote, *My twin, you are avoiding speaking with me because you'll cry if you hear my voice. I'm going to send you so many pictures of me without legs to make you cry some more.* That did it! Of course, I didn't want to see pictures; I'd rather call. I prayed for strength for a few minutes, and then called. As if she was waiting for my call, Joyce answered after the first ring. As soon as I heard her voice, the tears started rolling. I cried! She laughed! She was telling me to be strong, to be thankful to the Almighty, who has been her refuge and strength. The comforter became the comforted, and I was ashamed of myself. I was not ready to listen to her story at the time, but she told me the whole story from A to Z anyway.

While I was thankful for Joyce being in high spirits, I also prayed for her physical pain to go away. She had mentioned that she was still in pain and would still be in and out of the hospital for a while. I prayed for courage and strength for myself. Joyce made me realise that we are not defined by how we look, but by who we really are within. Later that week, I told her about a man named Nick Vujicic, whom she said she had never heard about before. Nick was born without limbs, but that has not stopped him from leading a full life.

Joyce became my hero. I told any friends going through physical, mental, and emotional pains, about this phenomenal woman. This woman who has accepted her physical body, the way it is. This woman who believes she now owes it to other amputees to help them accept their fate and move on with their lives, in the same way that she has done.

Joyce still does most of the things that she used to do, with joy and enthusiasm. She hops on buses to the market and shops all by herself. We chat on the phone when she's cooking meals from scratch, and I still wonder how she does this particular chore with some of her fingers amputated. I cannot wait to visit and see the awesomeness of the Almighty in her life.

Joyce is a dutiful wife and mother to her wonderful husband and beautiful children, whom she tells me have been her pillar of strength. The support from friends is because of who she is. She would do and give without expecting something in return. Givers never lack. When they give, they ultimately receive!

When Joyce told me her flat was ready and that she would soon move in, I was elated. That will definitely make life easier for her and the family. She sent me the video of the beautiful cosy flat this very morning. Thanks to all who made this possible, even though it took longer than expected.

I am happy that I am able to write about my dear friend, my twin, without crying or feeling sad. I'm smiling, and I am grateful to our Father Almighty for preserving her life. I am thankful for this amazing opportunity of being a part of this journey with my dear friend. I have learnt many lessons, and have helped a few friends by telling Joyce's story of faith, love, joy, hope, and peace. The Lord is! Glory to His Holy Name!

Oludotun Ademola

PRINCESS TENI AOFIYEBI

Joyce, I must say right away that I feel honoured to have been asked to make an input to your forthcoming book. No doubt by the time the reader has arrived at this section, he/she will already have had a full explanation of the wonderful and happy childhood you'd had with your loving parents and siblings in Abeokuta capital of Ogun State in Nigeria, up to the day you drove yourself to the hospital, and up to your current health situation.

You and I met at the age of 11 years ... were you that old? Anyway, I am your egbon (elder ... we still haven't got over that!). We were classmates and I believe roommates for all of our five years at St. Anne's School, Molete, Ibadan, now capital of Oyo State. Those were happy days in a school that gave us a very good and well-rounded education in music, art, cookery, domestic chores, culture, elocution, sports, etc. Your yellow house (St Clare's) sports dress had JOTO boldly written, with Kandahar at the back for identification. It should have been J. OTO because the letters were so bold that the space could not contain your surname. And so you earned yourself the sobriquet JOTO!

I recall that this was the name I called you, on the day I phoned you after I'd heard of your illness. I don't recall who told me or how I came to know about your illness. I didn't want to seem too serious, not knowing your state of mind, and having seen some of the horrific pictures put on GoFundMe.

Your incredible calmness and acceptance of your painful condition brought down the waterworks against my resolve to be strong for you. I was bawling down the phone, until you pleaded with me not to cry, but to rejoice with you for being alive. That did it. I had to excuse myself to call later. This was the pattern that our conversations followed, until I got a grip.

Once I had become used to the situation, I immediately took it upon myself to coordinate donations for your accommodation. It was of prime importance to me that you were able to wash, without having to travel to the hospital miles away to do so. After all, we Nigerians are used to having at least one bath a day! The task of raising money wasn't that difficult, as one look at your pictures melted everyone's hearts. People who never knew you were able to see your beautiful family pictures, and that lovely one of you sitting on the floor showing off your beautiful legs. Interestingly enough, a few of our classmates had difficulties coming to terms with your condition, and didn't know how they were going to talk to you on the phone. They felt they would break down, which would not have helped you. Ultimately, they braved it, and everyone was better for the experience.

Oh, did the old students of St. Anne's School rally round you! The show of love was massive. WhatsApp messages were being circulated by many class sets. Most gratifying was the younger sets that never even met us at school, particularly the ladies in the UK. They even arranged trips to visit you. Up school!!! Three gbosas!

The most wonderful aspect of your story, dear JOTO, is your state of mind. Your utter happiness and peace of mind, with the purpose that The Almighty has set aside for you, is inspiring. Your strong belief in your Maker has been your staying power.

I remember how happy you were the day you tried and succeeded in cooking Ewedu, although you tried to show me in the video that it didn't go slimy!! You were and still are self-confident and self-sufficient ... going to the market, shops, and hospital on your own, even at an early stage; not ashamed nor embarrassed at exposing your stumps in your shorts! JOTO! You made me a part of these trips with videocalls. I am so, so proud of you, girl, and I am glad I've been a part of this journey with you. I won't forget the agonising discussions we had over whether you would allow further amputations to be done. You would often get upset, and start venting. I understood, but always gently advised that you allow your doctors in their wisdom to do what they considered to be in your best interests. I'm happy that you eventually agreed. See how much better and happier you are? Now there's a brighter future ahead of you.

I rejoice with you that the council and whoever else responsible for your accommodation have finally commenced work. Hopefully, by the time your book is out, you would have long since moved in. I won't forget your anxiety and frustration over their very long protocols and foot-dragging. You, pretty lady, are a survivor and overcomer.

I still don't quite understand the cause of this strange and rare illness, even though you have sent me a video about it. But, knowing the Oyinbos (the white man) and science, hopefully they will find quicker intervention methods, and less drastic treatment in the near future. Keep on keeping on, dear one. Keep enduring and enjoying your physio, whilst staying on course for your goal.

Finally, I would like to take this opportunity to say a big fat thank you, once again, to all who responded to the GoFundMe cause or who made personal donations towards making life more comfortable for our friend Joyce Otolorin-Oluwole, aka JOTO. May we all continue to receive of His great mercy and blessings.

Princess Tenidade A. Aofiyebi

HELEN EFUE

His grace is sufficient …

Joyce and I first met at St. Teresa's College, Ibadan, where we both studied for Advanced Level GCE. We were both in the arts class. Joyce left for England a few months after we completed our A-Levels, to continue her studies.

After many years, we met again in Ikeja, Lagos. We both lived less than ten minutes' drive from each other, and spent many hours together several times a week. We attended the same church, the Household of God, pastored by Rev. Chris Okotie. When she had Ore, her son, and eventually decided to relocate to England, we went through all of those rhythms together. Her home in London became home to me and my children, whenever we visited London in those early years.

It is not possible to forget the day I received the news of Joyce's illness, and learned of her subsequent multiple amputations, through a message from a friend. To say that I was shocked to the very core is a woeful understatement. Numb with shock, it was a long time before I could check out the story for myself on the websites I was given – where Joyce's photos, before and after the amputations, stared at me.

Although the news had come from a reliable source, I had hoped that it was all a huge mistake. However, it was impossible to deny that this was indeed my Joyce. I could not imagine Joyce in a wheelchair and without her legs. The Joyce I knew was a busy bee, with fingers in many pies at the same time. My heart fainted as I tried to imagine the impact of this awful experience on her and her family. I feared for Joyce. I feared that she would be shattered, bitter, and miserable for the rest of her life. How does one so independent in mind and body cope without legs and several fingers? My mind was full of images of Joyce in her stiletto shoes. With the exception of winter boots, my friend never wore slippers or any type of flat shoes – and this had been the case even when I first met her.

For almost a week, I picked up the phone to call Joyce, but I aborted the call every time. Whenever I finally thought that I was ready, I faced another hurdle – the hurdle of what to say to her. What do you say to a close friend who has gone through such a horrendous experience? However, I started to fear that Joyce knew that I had heard, and would be wondering why I didn't call. So, one Sunday, flush with boldness and courage after church service, I called her number and she answered.

To my relief, Joyce sounded more normal and calmer than I could have ever expected. She told me the story of her long stay in the hospital. We spoke for hours. She said she was filled with gratitude to God for sparing her life. By the end of our conversation, I recognised that God had not only spared Joyce's life, but He had also given her the spiritual and emotional strength to cope with and rise above the challenges of her physical condition.

Since that first encounter, every conversation on any platform has only gone to reinforcing the abundance of the grace of God upon Joyce's life. Her post-amputation life is a vivid illustration of the limitless dimensions of God's grace. She is as busy as ever, being a normal woman, wife and mum – shopping, cooking, visiting hair salons and make-up counters in the West End, several miles from her house! I am not sure she ever had time to visit beauty parlours in those days when everything was normal. Each time we talk, she is telling me about one daunting job or the other she has just finished, chores that would be daunting for almost all other amputees, but not this one! Joyce has a strong spirit, and that spirit has put her in good stead since her amputations.

For a while, Joyce faced some challenges when the wounds were not healing as expected. Fortunately, the doctors intervened, and the situation turned around. Since then, her spirits have continued to soar. On the phone, you can tell that her laughter always comes from her gut. And on WhatsApp, her funny and witty comments always crack me up. As improbable as it might sound, I believe Joyce is much happier now than she was before her illness. You only need to hear her laugh or see her photos, to see what I mean.

Even with all this, the news that she wanted to visit Nigeria sometime in the future took me by surprise. Then, she told me that a book was in the works and near publication. She had kept it under wraps, but I soon took it all in my stride. It was easy for me, because I have since come to see many of God's promises and assurances playing out in Joyce's life since her amputations. To keep it brief, "…My grace is sufficient for you, for my power is made perfect in weakness." (2 Corinthians 12:9); "…With God, all things are possible." (Matthew 19:26); and finally, "And we know that all things work together for good to them that love God, to them who are the called according to His purpose." (Romans 8:28) There's no other way I can explain her ability to surmount her challenges and the joy that fills her heart every day.

I remember telling Joyce that I was certain God had a special plan for her. Although I myself did not see into the future at the time, I knew I spoke from the very depths of my heart. Who knows, perhaps this book and the book tour to follow are all Joyce wants or plans to do? Even these are huge achievements. Or perhaps there are more exciting projects ahead for this courageous and remarkable child of God.

Joyce, whatever you do, I will be here applauding.

Helen Irene Efue, Mrs.

KIKE ADEYEMI

I met Joyce in 1974. We shared an apartment together in London when we were students at South-West London College. She was a restless individual and always full of ideas. She still calls me 'Kate' to this day, after our boss at a holiday job refused to pronounce my similarly four-lettered name – Kike. I had no choice but to answer to this name and, 45 years on, Joyce still calls me Kate. Her love for excellence was insatiable. She was very strict – a no-nonsense person. She had so much energy, and was always jumping from one project to another.

Like any one of us, she had her challenges, but her spirit was never broken. She never allowed her situation to define her.

THE NEWS WE ALL DREAD

Late one night in the first quarter of 2015, I got a call from one of our mutual friends, Femi, that Joyce was in a coma in a hospital in London. I responded with multiple questions: 'What are you saying? Who told you? What happened? Are you sure you heard right?' Femi was unable to answer my questions, because the information she'd received was not comprehensive. We both agreed that Joyce needed our prayers. I promised Femi that I would pray, and let her know the outcome of it.

That night, I went on my knees and prayed for Joyce. The Lord laid on my heart these words: 'This sickness is not unto death.' I was so happy and delighted by this, and I immediately called Femi to give her the good news. For me, the matter was laid to rest – God was in control. There was no doubt in my mind that Joyce would come out of her coma.

A month or so later, a cousin of mine who is a friend of Joyce's nephew called me. He asked if I had heard what was going on with Joyce, and I said no. You can imagine my horror when he told me that both her legs had been amputated. I screamed! I knew Joyce well enough to understand that this would have devastated her – and I feared that she could end up becoming a shadow of her old self.

I called Femi for confirmation and the way forward. We agreed that she would call her husband and/or her brother for more information, as these efforts did not seem to be yielding any fruit. At some point in time, Femi said she would be travelling shortly to London, and would endeavour to see Joyce.

One afternoon in May/June 2016, I saw a plethora of missed calls on my phone – it was Femi. I called her back, and the first thing she told me was that she'd tried to call me while she was in the hospital visiting Joyce. She'd wanted me to talk with Joyce, but she'd already left by the time I called back. She then narrated what she saw, and how she burst into tears when she saw Joyce. To add salt to injury, Joyce was consoling Femi. Wow! That was unbelievable – yet I can relate to the unquenchable spirit of Joyce. After several tries, I eventually was able to speak with Joyce while she was still in the hospital. Although we did not have much to talk about, she was very appreciative of the call. I, on the other hand, was grateful to God that she was alive. We both ended up praising God for keeping her alive, and agreed that it meant God still had a purpose for her. I made a promise to visit her as soon as I could.

On my way to the USA in February 2017, I stopped off in London, to visit Joyce. On my way to her house, I was nervous. I didn't know what to expect. My cousin who went with me was also terrified. If he had a choice, he would not have gone with me! However, as soon as we walked through the door, it was obvious that everything about Joyce was normal. Really, it was quite unbelievable. She was herself through and through, to the extent where I had to comment on her unbroken spirit. Her husband and daughter were fantastic and very committed in assisting her. I was sceptical at first, to test if she was faking it, but she wasn't at all. She told me all the things she had done since she left the hospital, and I was amazed. She was going shopping for groceries and to the salon – for real? That tells you all you need to know about her spirit and faith.

Joyce's lively spirit and her strong faith shine in every way, whether that's on the phone or in person. She is a very strong woman, who finds the positive in every situation, and then attacks it with vigour. I hope that her book will inspire anyone out there who is feeling sorry for themselves; anyone who believes that they are at the end of the road because of their situation. Your situation is not the end, but a new beginning.

I strongly believe that there is no hopeless situation. As long as there is life, there is hope. Joyce, you are an inspiration.

Kike Adeyemi

OLUFEMI ODUSOTE

My name is Olufemi Odusote, and Sister Joyce is a friend. I got to know Sister Joyce at Kensington Temple in the mid-1990s, when I taught her son at Sunday School. As the years went by, even after her son had outgrown Sunday School, Joyce and I became good friends.

I didn't get to know about Joyce's illness for a few months, and just thought she was probably attending a local church nearer home. Then, one late Sunday morning sometime in August 2015, I gave a lady a lift home. It turned out, this woman used to be a schoolmate of Sister Joyce. During the journey, the lady asked me if I knew Sister Joyce, and I answered in the affirmative. She paused, then broke the news about the life-altering operation Sister Joyce had undergone. I have to say the enormity of what she said didn't really sink in fully.

When I got home that afternoon, I called Sister Joyce. She answered, and in the same breath began telling me right there and then that she'd had both her legs amputated. I have to say that the gravity of the situation still didn't really hit home yet. Anyway, I asked for the name of the hospital, and the ward and room number, and told Sister Joyce that I was on my way. I decided to make her a banana cake to cheer her up, and took other sundry snacks too, then headed off to the hospital where she was still on admission.

When I got to the hospital, Sister Joyce was lying on her bed, and loosely covered up. She recognised me immediately, and asked about my job and how I was. There were tubes everywhere. Although she looked quite weak and fragile, she was very much alert. Apparently, she had just emerged out of a long coma, so she couldn't eat anything solid yet and had to be fed through a tube. I noticed some burn marks around the tips of her ears and fingers, and I thought she must have been in a house fire and had rushed herself to the hospital. This is because, by then, I had learnt that she had driven herself to the hospital before collapsing.

I spent some time chatting to Sister Joyce, and then started to question her about the cause of her illness. She said the doctors couldn't even proffer a diagnosis yet. I was baffled by this, 'But they must have a team of diagnosticians?' Joyce said that every known specialist had come to see her, but none of them could offer a reason why this had happened.

I eventually left and went home. The next morning, the gravity of it all hit me. I actually had a meltdown; I was downcast and felt a huge sense of sorrow at what Sister Joyce had had to go through. I felt there was no justification for it. I couldn't understand why this had happened to her. I couldn't see the point of doing anything, and I just felt so forlorn. I stayed in my bed all day. Three days later, I went to visit Joyce again, but she was much weaker. Apparently, the effects of being a coma that long were beginning to take a toll on her energy level.

I have to say, Sister Joyce has an incredibly strong inner core. In all the time I've met with her, she's never shown any sign of bitterness, anger, self-pity, or fear. Although the road to her recovery has been arduously long and full of pain, she just continues to move on, planning ahead on how she can make a difference in the world. Some time ago, she said something that really put me in awe of her. She said, 'Since God has saved me, and I'm still alive, I've been asking God what He wants me to do next; how my life can be useful to Him; how I can be of service to Him.' Seriously, that floored me. Sister Joyce is indeed an amazing and inspirational person.

Olufemi Odusote

ABIMBOLA OPE-EWE

My name is Abimbola Ope-ewe. I am an old student of St. Anne's School Ibadan, founded 150 years ago. I also happen to be the immediate past president of St. Anne's Old Student Association in the UK (SASAOGA).

In the course of being the president of the Association, the situation of an old girl of St. Anne's was brought to my attention. The executive team and I then took it upon ourselves to see where we could be of assistance. Thus began my journey with this amiable, wonderful lady – Sister Joyce Oluwole.

Sister Joyce, as we often refer to her, was our senior, (as she was in the school from 1965-1969) while I, being one of the most senior in the executive team, was in St. Anne's from 1974-1979. But she relates to us as if we are classmates.

The executives visited Sister Joyce at home. We saw her situation, and we couldn't believe her spirit, even with her challenges. We reported back to the Association at the next meeting, and it was decided that we would assist financially to alleviate and make Sister Joyce's challenges a bit more bearable. Hence, we proceeded to donate to her GoFundMe appeal. To the glory of God, a substantial amount was raised, and then paid towards adapting her accommodation to suit her disability.

Sister Joyce has been an inspiration to all of us. We wonder, anytime we visit her, at the level of her spirit and joy in spite of her challenges. She always has one true-life story or another to share with us.

Sister Joyce has been in and out of the hospital on so many occasions with different challenges every time, but you know what? This wonderful lady refused to give up or be cast down. She is so much fun to be with, always so bubbly any time that me and others, such as Joyin Ayeni, Kemi Macaulay, and Lola Babajide Adenekan, visit her.

Sister Joyce is a determined individual, who believes in being happy – irrespective of what is going on around her. She attended the SASOGA Annual BBQ Family Gathering some time ago, and mingled very well with the old students of St. Anne's school, even those she had never met before. As a passionate volunteer of the UK Sepsis Trust, Joyce goes around talking to councils, schools, and churches to spread information about sepsis awareness and educate people about the condition. She looks forward to a time when she can visit Nigeria and Ghana, to make people aware of this killer ailment and how it can be "nipped in the bud". Hopefully, lives will be saved and amputations avoided.

I hereby congratulate Joyce on the publication of her book. This book confirms the kind of spirit she has. She wants to make people aware of this disease, so that help can be sought in the right quarters.

I pray for greater exploits, and I also wish her all the very best in her future endeavours in Jesus's Name.

Abimbola Ope-Ewe

My Real Legs

Photos of Sore Legs During Coma

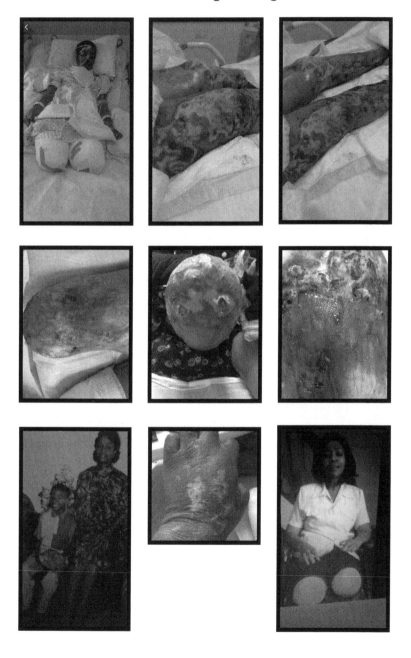

Healed Stumps – Back In Hospital

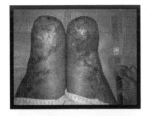

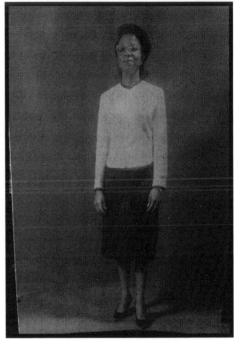

Healed Stumps – Back In Hospital

Stumps Cut Again – Prosthetic Process

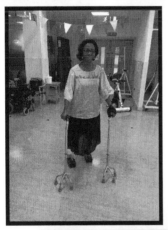

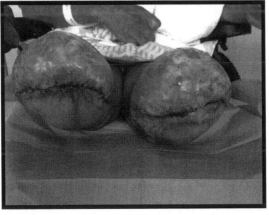

Limbs on Rockers, Limbs on Shoes

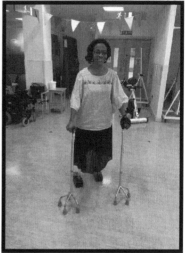

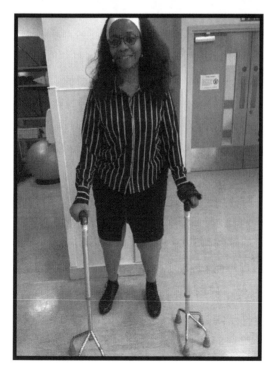

Cosmesis Lookalike Legs, with Changeable Shoes

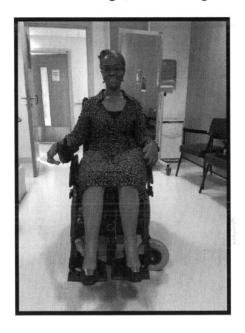

Metal Limbs in Shoes Before Cosmesis

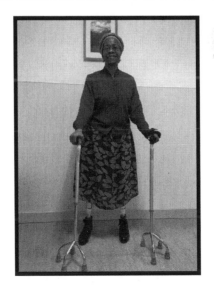

Out and About in Electric Wheelchair

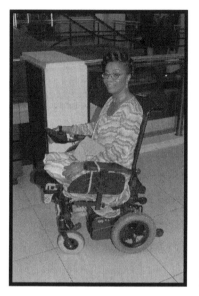

Holidays in Houston

Out and About at KFC with Tolu and Ore

Hot Water Burns, 2018

Cooking

Sweeping Up Leaves Outside

Opening Fuse Box

The Great Re-union 1965/1969 set,
St.Anne's School, Ibadan

The Great Re-union 1965/1969 set, St.Anne's School, Ibadan

The Great Re-union 1965/1969 set, St.Anne's School, Ibadan

The Great Re-union 1965/1969 set, St.Anne's School, Ibadan

Chapter 7 –

Home After 9 Months In Hospital

I was transferred from St George's Hospital to Queen Mary's Hospital on 5th October 2015, for rehabilitation prior to my discharge back home. I was at Queen Mary's for ten weeks. I learnt to sit upright at this hospital, after being on my back for the previous seven months at St George's. I was also taken to the amputee gym twice a day, for exercises to strengthen my core muscles.

After a lot of pleading, I was finally discharged on 17th December 2015. Prior to the latter date, they wanted me to go home for Christmas Day, and to return to the hospital following this, as I needed to complete some steps which would prove that I would be able to do certain tasks at home. However, I didn't want to go home for just one day. I wanted to be out of the hospital for good. Because of this, I was hurriedly put through some tasks. I had to show the occupational therapist that I could cook by myself, handle the gas fire, reach into cupboards, handle knives, pots and pans and anything else that was hot. I also had to show that I could wash items in the sink and use the microwave – all of these things without any assistance. With God's grace, I passed all of these tests, and was released.

It was great to be back home with my family. When I entered the house, I saw a single bed in the lounge laid out with pillows and blankets. The bed had remote controls to enable me to reposition it at will. My family and I gathered together to say a prayer thanking God for bringing me back home. At night time, I told my husband that I didn't want to sleep downstairs on my own while everyone else slept in their rooms upstairs. He said that he had bought a sofa bed for our young daughter, so she could sleep downstairs with me in the lounge, but I wasn't satisfied. I told him that I wanted all of us to sleep downstairs in the lounge. In hindsight, this seemed hilarious, but it wasn't funny to me at the time. I just wanted us all to huddle together now that I was back home after being away for nine months.

So, our son slept on the 3-seater settee, while our daughter slept on the sofa bed. She was quite excited about this arrangement. My husband and I "slept" on the single bed provided by the hospital. Well, we didn't get a wink of sleep. I was not yet able to lie on my side, and when I was lying on my back there was hardly any space for my husband. He was therefore halfway out of the bed, almost falling off. Yet he didn't complain.

In the morning, I told my husband that this arrangement wasn't going to work after all, and we agreed that everyone would go back to their rooms – except for our daughter who wanted to be with her mummy all the time. However, after a couple of nights on the sofa bed, our daughter became uncomfortable too; she wanted to go back to her room as well.

I found it difficult to accept that I would have to live in the lounge and sleep there alone, night after night. I felt alone and cut off from my family, and I just wanted them to be with me all the time – but that wasn't possible. Sometimes I thought I was selfish to expect them to forgo their comfort for me. But it wasn't just that, rather it was the fact that I had been relegated to the lounge because I couldn't go upstairs. I was annoyed, as I wanted to be in my bedroom upstairs and not in the lounge. It just didn't seem right.

My husband understood, and he was willing to keep me company by sleeping on the settee, but I felt that it would be unfair to him. So, I told him that I would be fine and he could go back to our room upstairs. I gradually got used to sleeping in the lounge, which was to be my bedroom for the next two and a half years. I knew that I had no choice, but when everyone said goodnight to me I would feel sad and just stare at the ceiling until I fell asleep.

Christmas was fast approaching. I needed to prepare, buy presents, and do the food shopping. That was something to look forward to. I insisted on us all having our usual Christmas dinner, and wanted us to celebrate it just like old times. However, I overestimated what I could do, especially after we bought the different foods for our Christmas meal. I was still very weak. So, on Christmas day, I sat at the kitchen table and gave instructions to our son, Ore, on what to prepare – including oven times and how to prepare the various foods. He was very happy to do it all, and he kept telling me that he was preparing Christmas dinner and that this was a big achievement for him. However, I wished I could do it all, as I became exasperated giving him instructions. We argued endlessly, because he felt that he knew a better way of doing things! That year, my older brother Freddie was invited to join us for Christmas. We had a sumptuous meal and a nice time together – just like how it was before my illness. Then we opened our presents, and it felt great to be back home.

I had a manual wheelchair, so my husband and my carer had to push me around in the house. In truth, I was completely dependent on other people helping me to manoeuvre. I couldn't do anything at will. Not being a very patient person, I soon learned to be patient and wait for help. This made me realise how fortunate I was to have good health and independence before I became ill. It also made me realise how I might have been taking things for granted.

In March 2016, three months after I came home from hospital, something strange happened to me. One night, I woke up to use my commode, but I suddenly realised that I couldn't move. I could not sit up and get onto the commode. I could feel my stumps, and that was a relief, but I couldn't move my pelvic girdle. Meanwhile, I badly needed to go to the toilet. I kept trying, until I became weak and had to let go. I had wet myself. Just as I tried to reach for my phone to call my husband who was asleep upstairs, I heard my son come in through the front door.

He looked at me and said, 'What's wrong Mum, why are you still awake?'

I said, 'You know that I won't sleep until you get in. Why are you so late getting back from work?'

He mumbled some explanation, but he knew that something was wrong, and asked me again. I then told him my ordeal.

He said, 'Don't worry, Mum, I'll help you to change your bedding.' He then carried me onto the commode, and got me a change of clothes, before putting me back on the bed. I fell asleep soon afterwards, but then I woke up at 5 am the next morning with a desire to use my commode. However, again I couldn't move, and I kept struggling until I wet myself again. By this time, I was beginning to feel sick, so I phoned my husband. When he got downstairs, I just managed to mutter a few words and (according to him) I drifted in and out of consciousness. So, he called an ambulance.

When the paramedics came, they asked my husband questions about what happened, and told him there and then that I must have a urinary tract infection – so they whisked me back to the hospital. I was on admission for about a month, and put on 5 litres of water a day, after they stopped giving me drips – as they said that I hadn't been drinking enough water. This was utter punishment, as I found it very difficult to consume so much fluid every day. Before my illness, I could just about manage to drink 5 glasses of water a day. I was finally put out of my misery a week later, when I complained to one of the doctors that I was so full on water that I couldn't eat 3 meals a day anymore. There were observations already that I was underweight at 44 kgs, and my weight needed to get to

50 kgs (allowing for my lost legs). Before my illness and before amputations, I weighed 57 kgs. With the above in mind, I had a dietician come in, and we both agreed on balanced meals that I should take. This included full English breakfasts! I liked this, and my husband was able to bring me some Nigerian food as well. I quickly put some weight back on, before I was discharged back home.

When I was discharged, I was given the assistance of a carer, to help me with my personal care and domestic needs. I refused to have a 24-hour carer. I felt that I didn't need that type of care, because it made me feel like an invalid. I wanted to learn to do things for myself and by myself. I got on well with my carer, and we were able to go to the market together to do some food shopping, but I insisted on cooking my own food every time. She helped me to stir food and to lift things – none of which I could do by myself. Hence, she was still with me most of the time, but in a way that allowed me to maintain some modicum of independence. Occasionally, I would ask her to escort me to the hospital when I had appointments, but she had other people to assist too. So, she couldn't come along with me as often as I liked her to.

One regular visit I had to make was to see Jane Holden – a specialist plastics nurse at St George's Hospital. While I was on admission, Jane would visit me in the ward and tell me at each visit that I had to get out of bed and go to the shower room to shower my stumps. She said that this would help my sores to heal. But, for some reason, I was scared to direct the shower onto my stumps. The sores (which were all over) were very fresh and still oozing in parts, and I felt that the pressure of the water from the shower head would make them hurt. Jane never gave up. She would say, 'You must shower these stumps, Joyce. It is the only way to quicken the healing of your wounds.'

I finally began to shower my stumps with the help of the ward nurses, as I couldn't hold the shower head. I didn't notice any change after this, but Jane did! After I got back home, Jane would phone or email me to see how I was getting on. I had to send emails to her every day about the dressings that were used by the community nurses, who came to tend to my wounds at home. Sometimes, they wouldn't use the dressings which Jane recommended, or they didn't even come at all. When this happened, I would phone Jane. She wrote several letters to the provider of these nurses, but the situation did not improve. So, I ended up going to see Jane at the hospital. She was very busy, but she did dress my wounds several times at the clinic. She said I had to return to the community nurses, because it was their job to dress my wounds, and wrote to them again.

Despite the repeated correspondence, the problems persisted. The community nurses still didn't come to my house when they were supposed to, on several occasions. I would phone them, and they would either say that I was not on their list that day, that someone would call me, or that someone was on their way to my house. It was frustrating to wait endlessly for them, so I started cleaning the wounds myself, as I had all the dressings at home. Sometimes, my husband would help me. But the oozing wouldn't stop. So, I decided to go to the A&E department at the hospital to ask for help. The nurses there were very helpful, and dressed my wounds every day for the next three months. However, there were still multiple problems, and not everything went smoothly. Occasionally, I would come across nurses who would refuse to treat me, as they said the wounds should be dressed by the practice nurse at my local surgery. They called the practice nurse several times, but she told them that she didn't have the time to dress the wounds every day. Appointments with her had to be made 3 weeks in advance.

I also had a terrible experience one day when I went to the department, to get my wounds dressed. The allocated nurse took me to a cubicle and told me outright that I was not an emergency patient, and so she was not going to dress my wounds. This was after she had pulled the existing dressings off. She didn't put them back on my wounds, and she told me to leave.

I couldn't believe my ears. I said to her, 'What on earth has nursing become?'

In response, the nurse told me repeatedly that I was not an emergency patient. I refused to leave after she dismissed me. So, she left me in the cubicle and disappeared for some 40 minutes. I suppose she thought I would have left before she got back. When she saw me again, still waiting, she called the plastic surgery department to see if they would dress my wounds – but when she got off the phone she informed me that said department was too busy, and that all she could suggest was returning to my GP.

By this time, I was losing the will to live. I was livid with anger. She had exposed my wounds and wasn't going to dress them. I told her that I wasn't leaving with my wounds exposed. She came over to me and covered the leaking wound with the bandages which she had taken off previously. At that moment, I was convinced that the devil had come to reside in her. I was fuming, and so was she. She disappeared again. I took the old bandages off and began to think of what I could do to cause a scene. I thought of falling out of my chair, but that would hurt my stumps. I wanted to scream, but I didn't think that would help, because her colleagues (including doctors) were going about their business and saying nothing. I had raised my voice before she left, so they heard me, but had done nothing.

The woman finally came back with a senior nurse in tow. This nurse asked me what I wanted, and I explained everything to her. She then turned to the nurse who was antagonising me and said, 'Can you please dress the wound and let her go'? She refused, and the senior nurse left. I couldn't believe what was unfolding here, and it didn't occur to me to take this nurse's name and file a complaint against her. A few minutes later she came up to me and changed the bandages without cleaning my wounds.

When she finished, she said, 'I am only trying to help you.'

I replied, 'Help? You don't know the meaning of the word. You are a disgrace to the nursing profession.' She chuckled as I left.

By this point, I had worked myself up into a frenzy, and I felt something was not right with me. I went to the entrance of A&E and joined the triage queue in order to see a nurse. When it was my turn, I told the nurse that I wanted to have a blood test. She didn't hesitate to give me one, as she could see from my records that I had been having regular blood tests. She did the test and my CRP (inflammatory factors) was high at 129%. A normal one should be 5%. She called a doctor and I was admitted immediately. I was on admission for 25 days. I narrated my ordeal to the sister-in charge of the ward, and she said that I should have noted that nurse's name and made a complaint against her.

From that point on, I always looked out for the nurse whenever I went to A&E, and I made up my mind not to let her attend to me ever again. Well, guess what? Eighteen months later, when I went to A&E, she was the nurse allocated to me. I recognised her immediately. I told her to get another nurse, because I didn't want her near me. She was shocked, and denied ever seeing me before that day. I reminded her of how she'd treated me the last time we met, but she said it wasn't her. She was adamant, and tried to take my history. When I refused to tell her anything, she called a doctor and told him what I'd said.

The doctor then said, 'No problem, we'll get someone else to attend to you.'

This time I got the nurse's first name from her badge, but not her surname. I saw her twice after that occasion, but she moved too quickly, hence I couldn't see her surname. Thereafter, I dropped the matter and put it behind me.

From March 2016, the aftermath of sepsis began to kick in. I was in and out of hospital admissions for various ailments, which came about as a result of the earlier illness. This meant that I wasn't spending much time at home, and when I was at home I had a very busy itinerary. I had to visit the hospital every day to get my stumps cleaned and dressed. I needed regular blood tests and other tests too. Sometimes, the ambulance would pick me up from home, and other times my husband would drive me to the hospital in his car. I had learnt to use a banana board to transfer from my wheelchair onto the passenger seat, with the help of my husband. I couldn't transfer on my own. I looked forward to making these trips, as I didn't have to be stuck indoors all the time.

Things I learnt and realised when I got back home:

- I became more aware of what we take for granted, and that we do not realise how fortunate we are to have good health.

- You need to let go of your anger. It is completely natural to be angry and resentful when you find yourself in a situation like mine. Clinging to these emotions will only make things worse, and they might make you ill too.

- You need to let go of bad memories and find peace with your condition. Once you accept the way things are, you begin the healing process.

- When you are back home from hospital, the real road to recovery begins. Try to take your mind off the past so that you can embrace the future.

- Ask for help from your loved ones, when you can't go it alone anymore. Don't suffer in silence.

Chapter 8 –

I Can Do It

When I was first discharged from the hospital, I was extremely reliant on my family to help me. I was still very weak, and continued to slump sideways in my wheelchair – a problem caused by weakened/wasted muscles – until February 2017.

During the nights I was hugely reliant on my husband, who I would call upon at all hours to help me onto my commode. Then, one day, when my sister Toyin was visiting, she heard me call out to my husband during the night. Instead of alerting him, she decided to come and find out what I was calling him for. I told her that I needed him to help me get onto my commode. As a retired occupational therapist, she went to work! She told me all about independence, and stood there and instructed me on how to do it myself. I got onto the commode, with a bit of a struggle, and I felt very tired afterwards. Then she said, 'Now, don't you ever wake your husband up at 3 am or anytime at that. You must start doing things by yourself and regain your own independence. Start exercising and doing the things you were taught to do while you were at Queen Mary's Hospital.'

That did it for me. I was happy to be able to do the things Toyin asked of me. She taught me how to get into my chair by myself, and wheel myself around. In actual fact, I realised that I had just assumed that I couldn't possibly do things, without attempting to do them first.

Before I left the hospital, I made a choice not to be depressed. I also resolved that I would wear prosthesis at some point in the future, which would enable me to walk again. I even made a decision that I would go back to work once I left the hospital. In fact, I was so keen on getting back to work, that I went back to see my office – where I used to work as an estate agent. It was only when I got there that I realised how weak I was. I knew that I wouldn't be able to work that job at that moment in time. My wounds hadn't healed enough, both internally and externally, hence I had to shelve the idea. But still, I did not give up hope. I never gave up on the prospect of getting back to my old life, and doing all the things that I used to do before I fell ill. I was totally consumed with the idea of living as if nothing bad had happened to me. I wanted everything to be just as it was. This wasn't easy for me, and I pushed myself so much that I would feel extremely tired by the end of the day. My son would say to me, 'What are you trying to prove Mum?' and my reply was, 'I can do all things through Christ who strengthens me' and 'Ojo Iku ni ojo isinmi.' *The day one dies is the day that one rests.*

For a while, I did think that everything that had happened to me was just a bad dream, and that my legs would grow back and everything would be just fine. Perhaps I was in denial, because to this day I have never given too much of a second thought to my leg amputations, although I often worry about my left hand where my fingers have been removed. In the earlier days following my illness, I would often get frustrated, because I couldn't hold anything with this hand. But my motto had always been, 'Never, never give up' – words spoken by none other than Sir Winston Churchill.

From the night where my sister taught me, I got on the commode by myself with the use of a slide sheet. I then gradually began to get onto my wheelchair without assistance. I was pleased with my progress, and I asked myself in my quiet moments why I had not tried to do this before. Well, I had a good reason; I was too weak to think about doing things by myself, let alone attempting to do them.

At this time, I only had a manual wheelchair, and so I still needed someone to push me around. The next thing I decided to try out, was to hold onto tables or walls and propel myself along the lounge and into the kitchen. This worked well for me, as I was able to get things done quickly, and so I didn't have to wait for anyone to help me move.

I also made a concerted effort to start cooking for my family. Previously, my sister-in-law, Mrs Bode Akande, cooked for my family while I was in hospital, and she continued to cook and send the food to us after I had been discharged from hospital. For this, I was most grateful, and I appreciated her help very much. However, by February 2016, I decided to do all of the cooking by myself. It wasn't easy for me at all. I couldn't grind the ingredients for cooking, and I still had to ask my husband and children to help me, but I persevered nonetheless.

One day, I moved too quickly, and found myself in the middle of the kitchen with nothing to hold onto. I was alone in the kitchen, so I began to look around me just to see how I could resolve the situation. My children were out, and my husband was in the bedroom upstairs. I stretched out my arms, but I couldn't reach or touch anything. I was simply stuck. I wriggled vigorously in my chair, but I still couldn't move close to anything that I could hold onto. Then, my husband suddenly emerged. He looked at me quizzically, and said, 'How did you get here?' And I replied with a chuckle, 'Just minding my own business when I suddenly glided into the kitchen.' He was aware that my manual wheelchair had a mind of its own, as it often moved by itself even when no one was pushing me.

A couple of months later, in June 2016, I got my electric wheelchair. This gave me the freedom I needed, so that I could move around the house and go out to do my shopping. On one of my first excursions, I went to a market in Peckham. I needed a long African broom, as I couldn't handle the vacuum cleaner. I used the broom to sweep, although I still couldn't get under certain objects. I tried this for a month or two, until eventually relenting and hiring a cleaner – who was able to keep the house clean in the way I wanted it to be. I also bought a small ironing board and a lightweight iron. Ironing was a difficult process; it took me an hour to iron a skirt, which resulted in my arm aching – but I felt satisfied that I had achieved something.

In December 2016, my daughter's Sunday School teacher told all of the children to bring some food to celebrate Christmas. My husband committed me, by telling my daughter Tolu that, 'Mum was going to do the cooking.' When they got back home from church, Tolu told me about it. I told her straight away that I wasn't going to cook anything, since I could hardly cook for the family. Hence I could not cook for a group of children. I then told my husband that I couldn't do it, but he said I could. Next thing I knew, Tolu and my husband went out together and came back with ingredients for the food that I was meant to cook.

I was upset, because I was left alone in the kitchen to get on with the cooking. I struggled with the grinder. I found it difficult to cut up the peppers, onions and tomatoes, and I kept dropping bits on the floor, but I was determined not to call either of them to help me. I thought to myself, I'll show them what I'm made of! I eventually prepared jollof rice, fried plantains, and roast chicken. When I finished, I felt so good. I felt that I had achieved something great. So, I sent messages via WhatsApp to some of my friends, telling them what I had done, and how happy I was to have been able to cook all of this food singlehandedly.

From then onwards, I knew that there was no reason for me to think or say, 'I can't do'. As a Christian, I remembered the verse which says, "I can do all things through Christ who strengthens me" and I still say this verse aloud every morning. I believe that God has indeed strengthened me.

If it wasn't for my faith, I would not have gotten this far. So, I want my book to encourage everybody. Whether you are disabled, an amputee, or going through some sort of pain or suffering – you can make a choice to rise above your difficulty. I know that it is not easy when you are in pain, but I believe that we are all spirits living in our bodies. We can therefore rise up out of our bodies, to alleviate our pain.

I would also like to encourage you, after you have made the choice to rise above what you are going through, to be more prayerful. I pray for strength every day. I pray that I will have the strength to make the choices which get me through every day, and to be happy – come what may. Happiness, I think, is a choice. No person can ever make another person truly happy, until said person has made up their mind to be happy. You alone are responsible for your own happiness.

Since I got out of hospital, I told myself that I was going to be happy and make myself happy, as I didn't know how much longer I would be on earth for. Mind you, after my amputations, I prayed daily asking God to help me not to get depressed. I believe that He heard me and answered my prayer.

While in hospital, although I wanted to be happy, and I prayed against falling into depression, I must confess that there were times when I didn't really want to live. I was in so much pain. But as time went on, I realised that it wasn't for me to decide whether I wanted to live or not. I knew that I was but clay in the hands of the potter. My Creator chose to set my life apart. He chose to give me back my life, and there was nothing I could do about it. So, I said to myself that if I was going to live, I had better make myself happy while I was alive – and just get on with it!

I do hope that as you read this book, you will feel motivated. Before I wrote this, I had met many people who told me that I had inspired them, because they were not expecting me to react the way I did to my situation. I certainly wasn't faking it. It was the Lord's doing, which was indeed marvellous in my eyes. I knew that I could not have remained positive in my own strength if God hadn't been gracious to me.

I remember that many of my friends who came to visit me at home and in the hospital were often in tears once they set their eyes on me. I would look at them and wonder why they were crying, and I would comfort them. My son would get upset that I wasn't crying, and I would tell him that I couldn't cry, as much as I tried. I told him that I just wanted people to be happy for me, because I had survived this traumatic experience. I wanted to be happy around people, and radiate happiness, because it is infectious. People around me would be happy if I was happy.

One of many bible verses which has held me in good stead over the years says, "Cast your cares upon the Lord for He careth for you." (Psalm 55v22). I also resonate with Charles Swindoll, who said the following, in his book entitled *The Finishing Touch*: "Virtually all of the things that once stole my joy and assumed my motivation – I just leave to God. Don't I care? Of course I care. But those cares are now placed in the hands of the One who can handle them. What once bothered me, I've learned to give over to Him who doesn't mind being bothered..."

Determined to pick up the pieces and take off again from where I was on 31st March 2015, I got back onto a mentoring programme in property in February 2016. Whilst I was ill, my estate agency business had fallen into ruin – I'd lost all of my business and thousands of pounds in revenue and rent deposits, because there was nobody to carry on with the business in my absence. My family, understandably, had more important things to worry about – coping with the idea of losing me altogether, and struggling with seeing me in such an awful condition.

My mentor helped me to set up a website for my property business. I was feeling stronger, and my purpose was to assist people to sell their properties and to earn a commission. I was no longer able to chase after tenants and see to the upkeep of properties anymore, but I was not the type of person to sit around doing nothing. I needed to do something to keep myself occupied. There were times when I would feel low, but it was different from when I had my legs, when I would really worry endlessly about something or get very angry. Anger was now fleeting at most, as was the feeling of sadness which would sometimes come over me. Yet that "sadness" was not because of my amputations. Really, I couldn't put my finger on the cause. Perhaps I was in denial, but deep down I did worry about my situation.

On one occasion, a D.I.Y crew from the BBC came to interview me, regarding my need for an extension to our home. A friend had contacted them on my behalf to ask if they could help me build an extension on the ground floor, since I could no longer climb stairs. During the interview, one of them asked: 'Have you had time to grieve over your loss?'

I was surprised by this, and didn't understand what she meant. So, I said to her, 'What loss?'

She answered, 'I mean the loss of your limbs and fingers.'

I laughed and said, 'Oh those! No, I haven't had a chance to grieve because I have been too busy trying to get on with my life.'

I must say that I have never grieved over my loss, and I hope I never do. I don't want to regress. I want to look forward to all the things that I can do to help other people who are either in my situation or similar. I want to help people who need to be motivated, encouraged and strengthened, in whatever situations they may find themselves. In my mind, the difference between 'I can do it' and 'I can't do it' lies in your mindset. Here's my take on it:

- Tell yourself, every day, that you are worthy of a good life. Make positive affirmations and believe in them.

- Your ability to be happy depends on your mindset, and your attitude to everything and everyone around you. Your happiness is lodged in your mind, and not in your circumstance.

- Always saturate your mind with positive thoughts, as these will sustain you in any situation.

- Re-programme your mind daily, so that it focuses more on what brings you joy and not sadness.

- Be totally committed to your dreams, so that naysayers will stop discouraging you and simply move out of your way.

- If you can only change your thinking, your life will surely change for the better.

- You need to arrive at a point where you can determine what's holding you back. Then, relocate your mindset to a place where procrastination will never find you.

- A mindset of defeat cannot lead to an empowered life. So work on your mindset first. Fix the inside before you try to fix the outside. The change you crave must begin from within.

- Changing your mindset is more important than changing your circumstances.

- Do your best to achieve something which gives you a sense of fulfilment; thereafter create your own happiness by following up on your passions and achieving them.

- What you think of yourself is more important than what other people think of you. So, let them think and say what they like. Who cares?

Chapter 9 –
Venturing Out

Every night, I looked forward to the moment that dawn broke – the start of a new day and a new opportunity to leave the house. I felt like a new being. During the time I was hospitalised, I never went outside the hospital. So, when I was discharged and had a chance to "see the world", it meant more to me. I appreciated it more than I had before my illness.

Occasionally, my husband would drive me down to the market to buy food. When my son took me out, we would go on the buses. I found this very exciting. The daylight simply intrigued me. I revelled in every single thing that God created: the trees in the park, the flowers blossoming in people's gardens, the birds. Everything reminded me of how blessed we are, even the shops. I would look out of the window with a longing to enter the shops and look at beautiful things. I marvelled at people's ingenuity, at the things they made, such as clothes, shoes, bags, and furniture.

The experience of going out was made all the more exciting once I finally received my electric wheelchair. Big thanks go to my occupational therapist, Melissa Jacobs, for this! It was just what I needed, and I began to dream of all the places I could reach with my new "Ferrari"!

At first, I was told to practise driving the electric chair around my home, and to try sitting in it for 2 hours a day. I was instructed not to go outside my home in the chair, until a wheelchair service engineer paid me a visit. This person was to escort me onto the pedestrian walkway, and show me all the things I needed to do and know about the wheelchair. Somehow, I totally forgot everything I was told about what to do when the chair was delivered to my house. I also forgot that I was told not to venture out before the engineer came to see me. When the wheelchair arrived, I immediately reached for the accompanying handbook. I went through the instructions with a fine tooth comb. I then got into the chair, swirled around the lounge a bit, and felt that I'd had enough practice. It was time to go out!

Needless to say, my son could not believe it when he saw me heading towards the door. He said I shouldn't go alone, and that he wasn't prepared to go all the way to the West End with me. I was determined to go out on my own anyway. When my son realised that I was going out with or without him, he got dressed and went with me on the first bus which I needed to take. Six stops later, I needed to take the second bus heading towards my destination. At this point my son got off the vehicle, and asked the bus driver to let out the ramp, which he did. My son explained to the driver that he didn't think I should make the journey after all, but the driver told him that I would be okay. Meanwhile, I stayed put in my chair and wouldn't get off. The driver pulled the ramp back in, closed the doors, and stopped. My son was still standing at the bus stop, staring at me in disbelief. I waved at him, and he kept talking to me, but I could only read his lips. I kept looking and waving at him as the bus pulled away. That was indeed a son's love for his mother, and I really appreciated his concern for me. But I was bent on going out anyway.

Ultimately, I needed 3 buses to get to my destination, and the journey lasted 2 hours in total. On getting to the West End, I felt as if I was in another country. The streets were buzzing with people and the shop windows were something to behold. Everything looked attractive to me. I went down the walkway, slowly taking everything in and enjoying the view. I finally got to Selfridges, went to Clarins and bought the cream I wanted. When I got outside, I decided to pop into a few other shops too, although I didn't plan to buy anything. Just knowing that the things I saw were available for me to purchase at any time was exciting. An hour or so later, I finally got my first bus back, and headed home. I'd had a very good day.

Of course, things didn't always go so smoothly. On another day, I had been out shopping for groceries, and I felt quite tired on my way back home. So much so that I began to doze at the wheel. I suddenly crashed into a lamppost! This was my first accident outside my home. I was quite shaken. My stump boards took the impact, luckily, otherwise I would have been seriously injured. At this time, my stumps had not completely healed, and they were still being dressed at the hospital every other day. I found it difficult to reverse away from the pole, as my stump boards were bent and stuck. Luckily, a passer-by asked if I was okay. She helped me to remove one stump board, and I was able to get home safely.

Despite this, I was never put off. I just wanted to be out there, whatever the weather. All I needed to do was to check the forecast and dress accordingly, come rain or shine. There seemed to be a driving force within me, pushing me to do as much as I used to do before I fell ill. People often told me that I was strong, and they marvelled at the things I got up to. Well, I might have been strong, but it was only by the grace of God that I was able to achieve these things. His grace is continually sufficient for me, and I draw on that Higher power every day. You can do the same.

During my travels, I usually found people to be very helpful. For example, people would sometimes approach me at the grocery store and ask me if I needed any help to get things from shelves. Most of the time, I actually asked for help, and people were willing to assist me. However, sometimes people would ignore me and pretend that I was not talking to them. I would usually approach a member of staff on these occasions. Even some members of staff would ignore me, but then I would pass them by and look for somebody else. I would say to myself that perhaps they were having a bad hair day! I just never gave up. I would ask and ask until someone listened to me. I certainly wasn't like that before I lost my limbs. I was far too impatient to be persistent.

One day, I lost my bearings on my way to a seminar in the West End, and I was very anxious because I was running late. I moved forward to talk to a man who was coming towards me. He had earphones on, and I beckoned at him. He stopped briefly to hear what I had to say, but to my surprise he just walked off. I had asked him where Alfred Place was. I expected him to either tell me where the street was, or say that he did not know. But he didn't say a word and walked away. I was a little upset by this, and I kept looking at my watch and moving forward in my electric wheelchair. I stopped other people on the same street and they simply walked hurriedly away. This was Tottenham Court Road in the West End! Perhaps people were not used to seeing wheelchair users in the vicinity. I felt as though I was not expected to be in the area – being disabled.

I then remembered Google Maps and stopped to check my location. I looked behind me, as I thought I might have passed Alfred Place. Suddenly, I saw a woman running towards me. She stopped and apologised on behalf of the people who wouldn't help me. She said she watched me from afar and then decided to run up and try to help me. I thanked her, and told her where I wanted to get to. Apparently, I had stopped right opposite Alfred Place. This lady helped me to cross over the road. There were roadworks everywhere, and the traffic lights weren't working. I was grateful for her help.

The following month, I decided to go to Regent Street in the West End. This time, I wanted to see the Christmas lights that had been switched on in November, as was the custom on that street. So, I hopped on the buses again.

I got there just as it was getting dark and the lights were already on. I got off the last bus at Oxford Circus and headed down Regent Street in my wheelchair. The lights were lovely, and I felt as though I was on holiday in a different country. I was very happy. Unfortunately, it was closing time at that point, and there were lots of pedestrians on the walkway. It got very crowded, and I was worried that I might get crushed. But one thing I noticed on the faces of many passers-by, was an expression of "What are you doing here?" as if I was not expected to be out in the area. I actually stopped and yelled out that I had every right to be in the area, and that I wasn't prepared to stay indoors all the time. I got a few stares for this! I carried on singing carols to myself until I reached Piccadilly Circus, which was about 5 stops from where I got off the bus. My husband was relieved when I arrived home, as he'd been worrying about me being out in the dark on my own.

On another day, I was on the bus (travelling a short distance this time) when a young woman with 2 children got on. She stood at the exit doors of the bus, looked at me and said, 'I wouldn't like to be in your shoes, I wouldn't like to be in a wheelchair like you.' I was taken aback by this, but I smiled and said, 'Well, I pray that you will never be in my shoes or in a wheelchair.' By this point, other passengers were looking at us. I followed up by saying, 'I'm happy as a lark being in my wheelchair.' At this, the woman's face dropped, and she looked very sad. I immediately felt sorry for her. I assumed that she was unhappy in her own life, as she couldn't seem to understand how I could be happy being disabled. Her kids were seated, but she remained standing near the double doors – staring at me – until I got off the bus.

On a more recent occasion, I decided to travel out of London on my own, to attend a 2-day seminar in Reading. I left home at 6.45 am, and got on a bus which took me to the rail station. When I got to the station, I went straight to the information desk and told them that I needed a ramp and someone to help me get onto the train. The staff were very helpful and asked if anyone had accompanied me. They phoned Reading station, and asked the station manager at the other end to help me get off the train. Everything went smoothly, but after I got off the train I couldn't find any cab with a ramp to take me to the seminar. I was very upset by this, and I went back to the station manager to see if he could help me. He finally got me a cab, after phoning round several taxi companies. I arrived at my venue fifteen minutes early, and I was pleased that I had made it on my own.

I had booked the hotel room for two days. After the seminar, I went to the front desk to check in. I was shocked when I got to the room and saw that the bed was very high. I wouldn't have been able to get on it. So, I rushed back to the front desk to complain. One of the managers went back with me to see the room. I told him to stand there and watch me get onto the bed. When I made the hotel booking, I told them what I required, and everything was confirmed as okay to me on the phone. The manager stood in the room and watched me struggle to get on the bed from my wheelchair. The bed was 28 inches from the ground – at least 8 inches higher than the seat of my chair.

We both went back to the front desk, and I threatened not to pay for the room; it was not suitable and the details had been misrepresented to me. By now, an argument had ensued. I had nowhere else to go for the night. It was obvious that I couldn't sleep in that room. That manager left and another one took over. He was very insulting, and even said that they had other disabled people who never complained about the height of their beds and that the hotel wasn't built with disabled people in mind. Well, that was it. I gave him the full length of my tongue and assured him that I would take the matter up with my local MP when I got back to London. The hotel's site stated that it was accessible to the disabled and had 10 rooms adapted for disabled persons. I really wondered how this hotel could have been granted permission to accommodate disabled people if all necessary criteria were not met. I insisted that I wasn't going to pay for the room, even though they had my card details. The manager said I couldn't stay there if I wasn't prepared to pay for the room.

My mentor from the seminar, who was staying at the same hotel, noticed that I was still at the front desk when I should have gone to my room. She came up to me and I told her what had happened. She spoke to the manager, but he was rude to her too. She then suggested that the hotel should put a sofa bed in the room, so that I could at least sleep that night. But for her intervention – I don't know what would have happened. Finally, I was offered a much bigger room, which could accommodate a sofa bed.

A very sympathetic housekeeper made the bed in my new room, and ensured that I could get in and out of it. She later told me that she had worked as a carer for disabled people prior to working at the hotel. Hence, she understood my situation and how I was feeling. When I checked out the following day, the previous manager was not around, and I narrated my ordeal to the manager-on-duty. She was very apologetic, and didn't believe the way that I had been treated. She offered me a 30% discount and promised to ensure that everything was okay at my next visit. I told her that there wouldn't be another visit!

Two days later, I received a request from the hotel to give a review about my stay. I narrated what happened, mentioned the name of the manager concerned, and suggested that he should be sent on a refresher course – so that he could learn once again how to treat guests and to remember that customers were always right.

All in all, I have had more good experiences than bad ones. One thing I do is to stand up for myself and be persistent when necessary. I love this quote from Mandy Hale:

'Strong women don't play victim, don't make themselves look pitiful, and don't point fingers. They stand and they deal.'

Chapter 10 –
Life After Sepsis

Although I am an extremely positive person, there were multiple side effects of sepsis which even positivity could not amend. Two months after my leg amputations, I suffered a stroke, and my speech became slurred. I also lost part of each earlobe, and the front part of my tongue. The right side of my mouth is permanently numb. By this point, you'll have some understanding of what sepsis is and what it can do to the body. Now, I will narrate the catalogue of illnesses which followed after I was discharged from St George's Hospital in October 2015, and also while I was at Queen Mary's Hospital too.

I was discharged to be admitted to Queen Mary's Hospital for rehabilitation on 15th October 2015. It was at this hospital that I learnt to sit up. I had been lying down continuously for 7 months at the previous hospital, because I was so ill and weak. I was taken to the gym at Queen Mary's, and had exercise sessions twice a day with the physiotherapist and the occupational therapist. Both therapists would take turns to sit behind me in order to keep me in an upright position. Whenever they moved away, I would slump. At the end of my nine-week stay I was able to sit up straight on my own in bed, and in a wheelchair. Praise God. I continued to slump sideways until early 2017, but my back got stronger and I was ultimately able to overcome this.

On my 62nd birthday, I developed severe inflammatory syndrome and hallucination as a result of UTI. I was immediately whisked away from Queen Mary's Hospital, back to St George's Hospital, where I was admitted and treated with strong antibiotics intravenously. Realising that I'd come in on my birthday, the nurse in charge ordered a birthday cake, which was shared with other patients and my family when they came to visit me later on that day.

I returned to Queen Mary's Hospital a week later. However, by the end of November, I was back at St George's for a blood transfusion – as my Hb was low. I was then sent back to Queen Mary's, when my blood had improved due to the transfusion. At this hospital, I developed a large wound on my right stump, which was infected by pseudomonas. This wound was dressed every day by the specialist wound nurse, but it did not heal until I was discharged. District nurses were instructed to come to my house every day to dress the wound, but after several months it still did not heal.

I had an appointment to see a team of doctors at St George's Hospital to hear their decision and conclusion about my condition. During the discussion, I told them that the district nurses were not consistent in their treatment of my wounds, and sometimes they did not turn up at all. As I explained in a previous chapter, this was a serious bone of contention and frustration for me. However, there was some really bad news to come at this meeting, which superseded my anger at the district nurses. The doctors informed me that I would never walk again, because my left hand – which I would need to hold a walking stick – was deformed. They said that I needed both hands to support me on the walking stick. This news hit me really hard, as I'd had my heart set on walking again in the future. I told the doctors that I wanted to cry, as I was so upset. However, I discovered that as much as I tried, I just couldn't do it. The tears wouldn't come.

Meanwhile, one of my fingers which was amputated in September 2015 simply refused to heal, and from the 11th January 2016 onwards, I had to go to St George's Hospital every few days to have it dressed. At the same time, I was sent to the hand therapy department, where I had various exercises to encourage me to use my fingers – although my fingers continued to cause me pain.

In the early hours of 11th February 2016, I was unable to move out of bed. Hence, an ambulance was called out to take me to the hospital. At the hospital I was told that I was febrile and tachycardic – whatever that means! I was again treated with strong antibiotics and I was discharged home on 17th February.

On 21st February, I was back in hospital on admission again. I called the ambulance myself, after 8 hours of pelvic pain. The pain radiated around my back all night and became very severe when I woke up. At the hospital, the pain lasted for a further 6 hours, and then subsided spontaneously without specific management. Both stumps were X-rayed, and the doctors concluded that there was "focal fuzziness of the cortical margin inferiorly in the medial femoral condyle, with underlying decreased bony attenuation." Yes, dear reader, I was just as confused by this as you are! In any case, they concluded that these features raised the possibility of bone infection – and needed further correlation with inflammatory markers.

After the pain resolved, I was discharged home the same day, but asked to come in as an out-patient in 2 weeks. This was the beginning of my weekly blood tests, designed to check the level of inflammatory factors in my blood. Sometimes they were high, which indicated that there was an infection somewhere in my body. At other times they would be low, which meant that I didn't have to take any antibiotics.

One weekend in March 2016, I realised that I had run out of pregabalin, which is the medication I use to relieve phantom pains in my fingers and stumps. The pharmacy didn't have it in stock, and the surgery was closed. I began to feel hot and cold at the same time, taking off my blouse and putting it back on every few minutes. Then, nausea set in. My eyelids became inflamed and I lost my appetite. Finally, the pharmacy was able to get a few tablets delivered to me at home. I took one dose, and within minutes all the symptoms that I had just disappeared. It was amazing. I had an appointment at Queen Mary's Hospital a few days later, and narrated my ordeal to the doctor. She immediately told me to stop taking pregabalin because of the reaction I had while I didn't take the tablets. She then recommended gabapentin instead. Initially, my phantom pains did not improve for about a month and I complained to the doctor. She increased the dose and said I had to stick with this new medication until it "kicked in".

On 11th April, the hand therapist concluded that my right hand was functioning well, and observed that I could use my thumb and middle finger to pinch things. By this time I was able to hold a pen and write – albeit illegibly. My left hand was still hurting though. I was told that the joints in my fingers had a fixed flexion deformity. I told the doctor that I wanted my fingers straightened, but was advised that an operation for my request would not be beneficial, as the pain wouldn't improve. In fact, I was told, it would actually make the function of this hand worse. The doctor who informed me of this said that he was in the theatre when I had the first operation, and that he and other doctors had battled to keep me alive – so he didn't want to take me into theatre again. He said any further operations could potentially have significant complications for me based on my previous history. So, we shelved that idea, although I was still not happy, as I couldn't use my left hand for anything. I prayed every day, and I still do, asking the Lord to release the muscles so that I can open and close my left hand at will. The pain is less now, but I am believing in God for a miracle. I remind myself that when the doctors gave up on me in April 2015 and said there was nothing further that they could do for me, God brought me back to life. God, who made me perfect in His image, is able to make good this left hand of mine, since the doctors can't do it.

While at the hand clinic, my stumps were checked. They recommended a different set of dressings, as the large wound on my right stump had not yet healed. I was advised to shower the stump prior to every dressing, as this would speed up the healing. Well, it didn't, and a month later I stopped – as I had something new to contend with. This time I was admitted to hospital on 9th May, for an abscess on the side of my left thigh. It was discharging what looked like pus. I had an ultrasound of my thigh, and the report stated that there was "heterogenous hypoechoic induration of the subcutaneous tissues", but no drainable collection was identified. It further stated that there was "extensive fat necrosis, chronic cellulitis sequential from my history of severe sepsis, multiple organ failure", and so on. It was a very detailed and long report, but ultimately the abscess was seen as superficial. I was, however, back in hospital on the 14th May, as the abscess was still oozing. I was given more antibiotics for the pseudomonas infection at the site. I was told to return to the hospital in a couple of weeks' time, for a review of the situation.

On 13th June, I was seen by the Pain Control Team, because my hands were swelling and very painful. I could no longer tolerate the discomfort of pressure dressings. I was told to continue taking gabapentin, which is supposed to relieve phantom pains. Then, on the 17th August, my scalp showed patches of scarring alopecia, and was very itchy. The dermatologist concluded that this was secondary to my previous sepsis and necrosis, and he prescribed Betnovate – which improved the condition significantly.

I was admitted to hospital again on 25th August, with left hip pain and fluid collection. This was drained, but I was kept in hospital for observation until 2nd September. I now had a break from admissions, and I had regular appointments at Queen Mary's Hospital for the possibility of wearing prosthesis. Well, this came with another set of problems. I began to feel that having sepsis was a "passport/gateway" to many an illness. Just when I thought there was something to look forward to – I got another bombshell on 21st October. The consultant at the rehab clinic had been informed by my plastic surgeon that a further revision of my stumps should take place prior to any consideration for the use of prosthesis. I had refused to have a further debridement of my stumps, simply because I was scared that I would lose the independence which I had gained so far. I also felt that I would be back at square one, going through all that pain again, if my stumps were cut. I was told that I wouldn't be considered for prosthesis until the debridement had taken place and the affected areas had healed. I was very upset by this. The doctors did offer me an alternative, of having cosmetic prosthesis instead, but I would never be able to walk in these, because they were just for show. Ultimately, I told them that I would consider it.

On the 8th February 2017, I went to see the plastic surgeon, because the phantom pains in my stumps were extremely painful, especially when they were cleaned and the dressings were changed. I had tightness in my toes, bilaterally, and cramps in my calf – both areas which were no longer there because my legs had been amputated. But somehow, my brain had not recognised that my legs were no longer there, hence I had these painful sensations. I could always pinpoint the exact position of the phantom pains. I would usually feel a very tight and painful pull on the third toe of my right leg, or a tightening around my ankle. It always felt so real.

On 25th February, I was admitted again, this time for osteomyelitis. I was treated with intravenous Co-amoxiclav. I had an MRI, which confirmed bilateral osteomyelitis and fluid around my left knee, but the radiology staff were unable to aspirate any fluid from the area to send to microbiology. My discharge from hospital took place on 14th March, with 6 weeks of intravenous antibiotics plus six weeks of oral antibiotics. The community nurses came to my house daily to administer the IV medication. Two days later, I developed a rash, and I was re-admitted to the hospital until 22nd March. I then developed some gastroesophageal reflux while on doxycycline. This reaction was awful, it felt as though my throat was literally coming away from my neck. My medication had been changed several times, but it appeared that doxy was still the best medication for the symptoms which I presented with. Hence, I was forced to take it for many months, although I also took omeprazole to counter the awful side effects. I prayed daily to be able to bear the after effects, which I must confess were getting me down. Finally, a blood test on 5th April revealed that my CRP (inflammatory factors) had dropped to 22%, from the 129% of several months before. I continued to have blood tests every few weeks, and my CRP kept oscillating, but I felt well in myself – hence there was no cause for alarm.

By this point, I had been told several times by the consultant plastic surgeon that I needed to have my stumps shortened in order to remove an exposed bone on my right stump. She said that I would continue to get recurrent infections if I didn't do this operation, and sooner or later I might lose much more length if the infection spread. What's more, she said I would then get sepsis again. So, I agreed to do the operation.

I was invited to the hospital a few days later for a pre-operation assessment. It went well, and I was told to expect a letter in the post confirming the date of the operation, which was 6th June 2017, and where to go. I was allowed to come in for an overnight stay on 5th June, as the operation would take place very early the next day.

On the day of the operation, the consultant who I had met previously came to talk to me. He told me, amongst other things, that there was a high mortality probability for the type of operation I was going to have. He wanted to know my thoughts about this. I told him that I wasn't bothered, that I was a Christian and if God so chooses He will call me home or let me live. I noticed that the consultant was taken aback by what I said. He left and said he would see me in theatre. Next, came the anaesthetist. She talked me through the process and asked me for my history, since she hadn't read my notes yet.

Lo and behold, when I got to theatre I was kept waiting for 30 minutes. The anaesthetist came in several times to tell me that my file couldn't be found. In the end, she said she couldn't put me under without knowing what happened on 28th May when my legs were first amputated. I was sent home until further notice. It then dawned on me that all things work together for the good of those who love the Lord. I thought to myself that perhaps God didn't want me to be operated upon that day. Maybe if it had gone ahead I would have died. Then I prayed, and thanked God that it didn't take place,

Two weeks later I got a call from the pre-op department, saying that some of my notes had been found, but the ones relating to 28th May 2015 were still missing. A couple of days later I got another call that the missing notes had been found in the hospital archives off-site. I couldn't believe this. I asked the man why and how this had happened. How could they have lost a recurring patient's notes? He couldn't tell me why, but he just apologised. I now had to wait for another slot to get the operation done.

Later that day I got a courtesy call from the doctor, Dr Y, who was supposed to operate on 6th June. I asked if he would now go ahead and operate. He told me that we should wait for his boss – Dr V – to return from vacation, and that one other doctor from orthopaedics would like to be present. My mind immediately flashed back to my conversation with Dr Y on the morning of 6th June, and his reaction to my answer about the high risk of death. I thought to myself that he must have been nervous and didn't want to go ahead without his boss in attendance. Overall, I thanked God once again for sparing me the ordeal of another operation. At this point, I was actually convinced that God didn't want me to undergo another operation in spite of advice from several doctors involved with my care. Well, God moves in mysterious ways, and His thoughts are not our thoughts.

When Dr V arrived back from vacation, I got a call that she would be operating as soon as a slot was available. Then, when Dr V and Dr Y were available, the third doctor wasn't. I just felt fed up.

Ultimately, the third doctor (who was from orthopaedics) decided that it wasn't necessary for him to be present at my operation. This message was passed on to me by the pre-op assessment department. Now I began to learn to be patient and wait for the Lord to arrange everything according to His purpose. Next, Dr Y decided to take a week off work, so Dr V was the only one available, but she said she needed Dr Y to assist – as the operation could take over 4 hours. I concurred and continued to wait. I prayed for the two doctors to be available at the same time, so we could get it done and over with.

As there was still no date in sight, at the end of June 2017 I asked my GP if he could assist me in getting off my phantom pain medication – because it had caused me to put on a lot of weight, especially around my midriff. I showed him my protruding stomach and told him that I looked eight months pregnant. He agreed that I should go off the medication, but gradually. I did this, and joined a gym, where I had a personal trainer and was weighed every fortnight. I finally lost 2 kg in one month. I was pleased that my stomach had gone down, but I needed to lose more weight in order to get back into my size 12 clothes. I was now a size 16 in tops and size 18 in skirts and trousers.

Sometime in August 2017, I received a call from the pre-op department informing me of an available slot for my operation to take place. I was told to come in for another pre-op procedure. I told the caller that I had done one recently, before the date scheduled for my operation on 6th June was cancelled, hence I didn't think that I needed to have another one so soon. He chuckled, and said that I had to come in again, otherwise the operation wouldn't take place. So, I agreed to come in.

About three weeks before the operation was due, I got on a bus and headed for the West End. I was happy, and I looked forward to getting my usual face essentials from Selfridges. Suddenly, about 2 miles from my home, I fell into the depths of despair. A dark gloom enveloped me, and I didn't understand why I'd had this sudden mood change. I began to pray that God would remove the need for the operation and heal the intermittent leaking from my stumps. At the same time, I prayed that God would make it possible for me to wear prosthesis in spite of the exposed bone sticking out of my right stump. I kept asking myself what could have caused the sad feeling I was getting. I couldn't get an answer, so I began to ask God to remove the feeling from me. I remember saying, 'The joy of the Lord is my strength' over and over again until I reached my destination. By the time I got to the shop, the feeling of sadness had disappeared – but I kept asking myself why it came over me in the first place. But I found no answer, and I forgot all about it.

Two days later I got the sad feeling again, but stronger this time, and it stayed with me for 3 weeks. I told my husband, and he said perhaps I was worried about the pending operation. But I said I wasn't, yet I didn't know what was wrong. I tried to see my GP, but he was away on holiday. I wanted him to tell me what was wrong with me, because I simply didn't know.

The sad feelings made me lethargic, and I began to see everything as a chore. I kept praying for this feeling to pass, and I had to force myself to do things like cooking, eating, and cleaning. By this time I had become very anxious too. I reminded myself constantly of Paul's words from the Bible, "I can do all things through Christ who strengthens me", and our Lord's own words, "Let not your heart be troubled, neither let it be afraid."

By this point I had stopped sleeping well at night, so I would repeat Isaiah's words from the Bible, "Fear not I am with you, I will uphold you with my victorious right hand."

Suddenly, the Bible verses which I had memorised many years ago began to come back to me, and they were more real than before. I kept counting the days when my GP would return to the practice, as I did not want to see any other doctor, although I prayed that God would lift the sad feeling from me. During this period, I went online to find some alternative medicines which might help me. In doing so, I found lavender oil. I put a few drops of this on my handkerchief, and sniffed it throughout the day and before I went to bed. It helped with my anxiety, but the gloomy feeling did not go away.

My GP finally got back to the practice 4 days before my scheduled operation. I told him all that had happened. He concluded that the medication which I had weaned myself off might be responsible, as well as the fact that I was due for another major operation. He said the situation was beyond my control, and that there was nothing I could do about it. I immediately told myself that the situation was under God's control, and I would continue to pray to Him to help me.

D-day for my operation arrived on the 6th September 2017. I had the chance to talk to one of the doctors before I was taken to theatre. I told her about my experience during the previous 3 weeks. As I was still holding my hanky and breathing the lavender oil intermittently, she said I could keep it with me in theatre. When I came round after the operation, the sadness and anxiety had completely left me. I felt like myself again, and I thanked God for his blessing in seeing me through this.

This operation turned out to be a blessing in disguise. I recuperated fully within three weeks, and I had my wounds dressed at the hospital. There was no more leaking or infections. From this time onwards, I simply went from strength to strength. No more hospital admissions – I felt very well. I could now concentrate on getting my prosthesis.

On 4th December 2018, I wore my prosthesis to my appointment with the consultant plastic surgeon who had operated on my stumps. Her colleague, Dr S, was the first person to spot me in the corridor – so he went to the consultant's room and told her that I had my stilts on. The consultant then came out surrounded by nurses and other doctors, and asked me to walk towards her. I proudly did so, and she took a video of me walking. Everyone started to clap their hands and cheer me on. We went into her office and she said, 'Well done. You proved me wrong!' All's well that ends well.

My post-hospital period from December 2015 to September 2017 was very traumatic for me, as I was in and out of admissions many times. I thank God for His grace over my life and for His triple portion of favour: (1) He spared my life, (2) He healed me, (3) He made me very happy in spite of my amputations. May the Lord be Praised. Amen.

Chapter 11 –

A Dream Come True

I do not begrudge the doctors at the hospital, nor the specialist nurses, physiotherapists and occupational therapists, all of whom said that I would never walk again, even with the use of prosthesis. They believed that the skin on my stumps was extremely fragile, and would break under the strain of a prosthetic limb. At the end of the day, all of these professionals were simply doing their job – based on their knowledge and experience. It is only by the grace of God that I have accomplished this feat of walking again. It is truly a miracle, and a testament to His magnificence.

When the doctors at the hospital finally agreed to sit down and have a formal meeting about the use of prosthesis, since I was so persistent, I was relieved. Finally, I would have a chance to show that this was the right option for me. The meeting was made up of all the professionals who had said there was no chance of me walking again. I was told to get on a plinth in the doctor's room, while the physiotherapist put me through some rigorous exercises. My stumps really hurt while doing this, but I didn't show it for fear of failing the assessment. They were all surprised at my performance. I remember that the occupational therapist apologised to me on behalf of the team, for saying that I could never walk again.

In my quest to walk again, I prayed to God every day, and reminded Him that when He made me, he made me perfect and in His own image. Also, when the doctors said there was nothing further that they could do to save me, this same God took over and brought me back to life. I learned that when humans reach the end of their tether, that is when God takes over and completes His work by Himself. This time they said I couldn't walk, but I believed that my God would come through. I also reminded myself of His words:

"For with God nothing shall be impossible" (Luke 1:37); and "God is not a man, that He should lie; neither the son of man, that he should repent: hath He said, and shall He not do it? Or hath he spoken, and shall He not make it good?" (Numbers 23:19)

Following the meeting, I received a letter from the hospital, asking me to attend the prosthesis department in two weeks' time. I went there, and my stumps were measured and cast! I was very happy, and asked the nurses to take pictures of the casts when they were taken off. I was then told to come back for a fitting. This time, plastic tubes had been made to my size and filled with casting cement, up to the point where the end of my stumps would rest. The nurses helped me to put them on. I was elated. Then, they helped to lower me to the floor so I could stand upright. There I was, standing, after 3 years. I was excited and nervous at the same time. I tried to walk but they stopped me. It was too early for that. When I got home, I thanked God for the experience, and asked Him to continue to strengthen my stumps and help me to walk with ease. I had been told by the nurses that the casts were heavy, but I didn't care. I simply told myself that, 'I can do all things through Christ who strengthens me.' I went back to the hospital every day to practise walking in my casts. I needed to get used to these, before the prosthetic legs were made. I even thought to myself that I might be ready to wear shoes soon!

Finally, my prosthetic legs were ready. I went to the hospital amputee gym from Monday to Friday, to practise using my new legs for the next three months. The sessions lasted for five hours, with a one-hour break for lunch in between times. I would be told to get on the plinth in a cubicle and lie down. Then the physiotherapist would put me through some exercises designed as a "warm up" before I could wear my new legs.

The legs were heavy, and because some of my fingers were amputated, I was unable to lift them up and put them on by myself. However, I managed to get the rubber pressure liners on by myself. These had a snug fit and were meant to protect my stumps from rubbing against my new legs. My stumps were badly scarred, and the skin covering them was very fragile, hence they were prone to breaking. The physiotherapist would then help me to put on the legs, which were attached to a band that went around my waist. She would then fasten the bands, one in front and another at my back, to a Velcro attachment to hold them together securely. Now, I was ready to walk.

First, I needed to get back into my chair and wheel myself to the bars. Here, I would park my chair in-between two parallel bars, hold onto the bars, and lift myself up from my chair. Then I would start walking, taking one step at a time, and looking in the mirror which was in front of me. I was always encouraged by the physiotherapist and fellow amputees who shouted, 'Come on Joyce, come on gal, you can do it.' They would even clap when I was able to walk down the whole length of the room unaided! I always asked the physiotherapist to take pictures of me walking, and to film my progress at each visit to the gym. I felt confident and happy that I had proved that I could walk after all.

By April 2018, I was allowed to take my prosthetic legs home, with rockers attached as feet. The rockers helped me to find my balance, but I didn't like them much, because they were blocks shaped like feet facing the opposite direction. In short, they were ugly to behold. I practised walking around the house and in my garden every day for about an hour. I wanted to do this in order to strengthen my core, and as a form of exercise, so that I wasn't sitting in my chair all the time.

Three months later, I received a letter from the hospital, inviting me to attend a review. I passed the review and asked for "feet". This request was not granted, as the physiotherapist said that I wouldn't be able to walk with feet. I was adamant, and asked the doctor to intervene. I was finally told that I needed to wear the legs for around 4 or 5 hours a day, and then come back in 6 weeks for another review. I went back for the review, having worn the legs for 3 to 4 hours a day. One would think they'd have given me feet after this, but no, they didn't. I had another meeting with the doctor, the prosthetist, and a physiotherapist, and they decided to give me knees instead – which would make me a couple of inches taller. I agreed to this, as these would enable me to wear my legs on the buses without inconveniencing other passengers. I would be able to bend my knees on the bus. Also, I could now reach shelves in my house and in the shops.

I was now about five foot seven inches in height – three inches taller than I was before my amputations. I felt **too** tall though, and a few weeks later, I asked to be made shorter and asked for feet again. I was told to come back in six weeks when a pair of feet would have been ordered for me. I was told to bring in several pairs of shoes and the most suitable for my new feet would be selected. Wow! Talk about persistence. Well, it paid off.

My appointment to have my feet fitted finally took place on 24th January 2019. I took two pairs of two-inch block heel shoes, and one pair of ankle boots with a half-inch heel. The latter was selected and put on my new feet. The physiotherapist assisted me as usual with putting my legs on. I stood up, feeling very pleased with myself, standing tall and wearing shoes for the first time in three years and nine months! I had my picture taken, and I was filmed trying to get up from my chair to start walking.

It wasn't long before I began to ask for something more. I had heard of cosmesis, and I wanted that too. This is an outer aesthetic covering on a prosthesis – to make it look more natural. I saw several outpatients in the amputee gym who had cosmesis on their artificial limbs. It was almost impossible to tell that their limbs were not natural. The limbs looked very natural on patients who didn't use any walking aids, and those who did use walking aids looked good too.

At my next appointment in March, I shall be pushing for cosmesis, as well as another pair of legs and feet – which will have a ridge enabling me to wear my two-inch heeled shoes as well.

Wish me luck!

Chapter 12 –

Personalised Bible Verses

After spending four months in the Intensive Care Unit at St George's Hospital, I was moved to the McEntee Ward, where I was placed in a room all by myself. The first thing I noticed in this room, was that there were pictures of my children and a family photo of all of us, on the windowsill. I was told that the doctors had asked my husband to bring in the photos while I was in a coma, in ICU. The intention was for these pictures to aid my recovery. But I don't remember anything from when I was there, except my coma, which I have already narrated.

As I lay in bed in this room, I would quote Bible verses that I had memorised since 1977. I had a Bible with me, but I was too weak to hold it and open it. At this time, I would drop anything I attempted to hold. When my phone rang, the nurses would pick it up for me, and they would hold it close to my ears so I could speak to the caller.

I tried to remember the verses which would be most appropriate to what I was feeling and thinking at any point in time. I was afraid, not of death, but of the loneliness I felt at night. I was unable to sleep, due to the pain in my stumps. I often spoke verses aloud, such as, "Give me sleep Lord because I am your beloved" (Psalm 127:2), "Peace I leave with you, my peace I give unto you: not as the world giveth, give I unto you. Let not your heart be troubled, neither let it be afraid" (John 14:27). Another one was "Have no anxiety about anything, but in everything by prayer and supplication with thanksgiving, make your requests known to God" (Philippians 4:6).

I could not say any proper prayers, except asking God to prevent me from falling into depression as a result of my amputations. Strangely, I don't remember ever asking God to heal me while I was on admission in hospital. But in His mercy, He healed me. I remember that my family and friends would pray for me whenever they visited me – just before they left my bedside. Looking back, I think I must have been shocked by everything that happened. Hence, I spent most of the time thinking about the pain I was experiencing. Somehow, I only imagined an end to the pain, if only God would call me Home. On bad days, I would say 'O death, where is thy sting? O grave where is thy victory.' (1 Corinthians 15: 55) followed by a song: 'Nipa ife Jesu Christi ki yio si nkan.' *Through the love of God our Saviour, all will be well.* My heart was constantly in turmoil, so I spoke this verse out loud: 'Have no anxiety about anything but by prayer and supplication with thanksgiving make your requests known to God.' (Philippians 4:6)

In August 2015, my older sibling, Sister Toyin, bought me a "reader". This was placed over my hospital bed, with my Bible affixed to it, so I could read my Bible without holding it. I was very happy for this, and I was able to personalise certain verses as I read them. These verses held me in good stead during my illness, and even now I continue to draw my strength from them daily. I hope you can too. I have written down each verse on small cards, and I carry them around in my handbag to read anywhere, everywhere and at any time.

Here are the personalised ones:

THIS SICKNESS OF MINE IS NOT UNTO DEATH.
(JOHN 11 V 4)

I CAST ALL MY ANXIETIES UPON HIM FOR HE
CARES ABOUT ME.
(1 PETER V5 7)

I CAN DO ALL THINGS THROUGH CHRIST WHICH
STRENGTHENETH ME.
(PHILIPPIANS 4 V 13)

THIS IS THE DAY WHICH THE LORD HAS MADE, I
WILL REJOICE AND BE GLAD IN IT.
(PSALM 118 V 24)

NO WEAPON THAT IS FORMED AGAINST ME SHALL
PROSPER, AND I CONDEMN EVERY TONGUE THAT
RISES UP AGAINST ME IN JUDGEMENT.
(ISAIAH 54 V 17)

BUT MY GOD SHALL SUPPLY ALL MY NEED
ACCORDING TO HIS RICHES IN GLORY BY
CHRIST JESUS.
(PHILIPPIANS 4 V 19)

WHAT THINGS SO EVER I DESIRE, WHEN I PRAY,
I BELEIVE THAT I RECEIVE THEM AND I SHALL
HAVE THEM.
(MARK 11 V 24)

FOR GOD HASNOT GIVEN ME A SPIRIT OF FEAR
BUT OF POWER AND OF LOVE AND OF A
SOUND MIND.
(2 TIMOTHY 1 V 7)

IF I HAVE FAITH, NOTHING SHALL BE IMPOSSIBLE
UNTO ME.
(MATHEW 18V 20)

THE LORD IS MY HELPER, I WILL NOT BE AFRAID.
WHAT CAN ANYONE DO TO ME.
(HEBREWS 13 V 6)

I REJOICE EVERMORE. I PRAY WITHOUT CEASING.
I GIVE THANKS IN EVERYTHING: FOR THIS IS THE
WILL OF GOD IN CHRIST JESUS CONCERNING ME.
(1 THESSALONIANS 5 V 16-18)

...IF GOD BE FOR ME, WHO CAN BE AGAINST ME.
(ROMANS 8 V 31)

AND IT SHALL COME TO PASS, THAT BEFORE I
CALL, HE WILL ANSWER: AND WHILE I AM YET
SPEAKING, HE WILL HEAR.
(ISAIAH 65 V 24)

THOUGH HE WAS RICH BUT FOR MY SAKE, HE
BECAME POOR, SO THAT BY HIS POVERTY, I MIGHT
BECOME RICH.
(2 CORINTHIANS 8 V 9)

GOD IS MY STRENGTH AND POWER AND HE
MAKETH MY WAY PERFECT.
(2SAMUEL 22 V 33)

BEHOLD GOD IS MY SALVATION, I WILL TRUST AND
NOT BE AFRAID.
(ISAIAH 12 V 2)

I HAVE SET THE LORD ALWAYS BEFORE ME,
BECAUSE HE IS MY RIGHT HAND, I SHALL NOT
BE MOVED.
(PSALM 16 V 8)

THE LORD IS MY LIGHT AND MY SALVATION,
WHOM SHALL I FEAR, THE LORD IS THE STRENGTH
OF MY LIFE OF WHOM SHALL I BE AFRAID.
(PSALM 27 V 1)

BUT HE KNOWETH THE WAY THAT I TAKE, WHEN
HE HATH TRIED ME, I SHALL COME FORTH AS
GOLD.
(JOB 23 V 10)

CREATE IN ME A CLEAN HEART, O GOD AND
RENEW A RIGHT SPIRIT WITHIN ME.
(PSALM 51 V 10)

Other Bible Verses That Have Helped Me:

FEAR THOU NOT; FOR I AM WITH THEE: BE
NOT DISMAYED; FOR I AM YOUR GOD: I WILL
STRENGTHEN THEE; YEA, I WILL HELP THEE; YEA,
I WILL UPHOLD THEE WITH THE RIGHT HAND OF
MY RIGHTEOUSNESS.
(ISAIAH 41 V 10)

BE SOBER, BE VIGILANT, BECAUSE YOUR
ADVERSARY THE DEVIL AS A ROARING LION,
WALKETH ABOUT, SEEKING WHOM TO DEVOUR.
(1 PETER 5 V 8)

FOR YE HAVE NEED OF PATIENCE AFTER YE HAVE
DONE THE WILL OF GOD, YE MIGHT RECEIVE THE
PROMISE.
(HEBREWS 10 V 36)

LET US THEREFORE COME BOLDLY UNTO THE
THRONE OF GRACE, THAT WE MAY OBTAIN MERCY
AND FIND GRACE TO HELP IN TIME OF NEED.
(HEBREWS 4 V 16)

YEA, THOUGH I WALK THROUGH THE VALLEY OF
THE SHADOW OF DEATH, I WILL FEAR NO EVIL:
FOR THOU ART WITH ME; THY ROD AND THY
STAFF THEY COMFORT ME.
(PSALM 23 V 4).

WHEN THOU PASSEST THROUGH THE WATERS, I
WILL BE WITH THEE; AND THROUGH THE RIVERS,
THEY SHALL NOT OVERFLOW THEE: WHEN THOU
WALKEST THROUGH THE FIRE, THOU SHALT NOT
BE BURNED; NEITHER SHALL THE FLAME KINDLE
UPON THEE.
(ISAIAH 43 V 2)

I WILL INSTRUCT THEE AND TEACH THEE IN THE
WAY WHICH THOU SHALT GO. I WILL GUIDE THEE
WITH MINE EYE.
(PSALM 32 V 8)

THE LORD IS GOOD, A STRONGHOLD IN THE DAY
OF TROUBLE AND HE KNOWETH THEM THAT
TRUST IN HIM.
(NAHUM 1 V 7)

IN THE NAME OF OUR LORD JESUS CHRIST,
ALWAYS GIVE THANKS FOR EVERYTHING TO GOD
THE FATHER.
(EPHESIANS 5 V 20)

DELIGHT THYSELF ALSO IN THE LORD; AND HE
SHALL GIVE THEE THE DESIRES OF THINE HEART.
(PSALM 37 V 4)

REMEMBER THAT I HAVE COMMANDED YOU TO BE
DETERMINED AND CONFIDENT. DON'T BE AFRAID
OR DISCOURAGED FOR I THE LORD YOUR GOD AM
WITH YOU WHERE EVER YOU GO.
(JOSHUA 1 V 9)

FOR I KNOW THE THOUGHTS THAT I THINK
TOWARD YOU....THOUGHTS OF PEACE AND NOT
EVIL, TO GIVE YOU AN EXPECTED END.
(JEREMIAH 29 V 11)

SEEK YE THE LORD WHILE HE MAY BE FOUND,
CALL YE UPON HIM WHILE HE IS NEAR.
(ISAIAH 55 V 6)

IF ANY OF YOU LACKS WISDOM LET HIM ASK
GOD WHO GIVES TO ALL MEN GENEROUSLY
AND WITHOUT REPROACHING AND IT WILL BE
GIVEN HIM.
(JAMES 1 V 5)

BE STRONG AND OF GOOD COURAGE, FEAR
NOT, NOR BE AFRAID OF THEM FOR THE LORD
YOUR GOD, HE IT IS THAT DOTH GO WITH THEE,
HE WILL NOT FAIL THEE, NOR FORSAKE THEE.
(DEUTERONOMY 31 V 6)

BUT THEY THAT WAIT UPON THE LORD SHALL
RENEW THEIR STRENGTH; THEY SHALL MOUNT
UP WITH WINGS AS EAGLES, THEY SHALL RUN
AND NOT BE WEARY AND THEY SHALL WALK
AND NOT FAINT.
(ISAIAH 40 V 31)

VERILY, VERILY, I SAY UNTO YOU, WHATSOEVER
YOU SHALL ASK THE FATHER IN MY NAME HE WILL
GIVE IT TO YOU.
(JOHN 16 V 23)

I ALONE KNOW THE PLANS I HAVE FOR YOU, PLANS TO BRING YOU PROSPERITY AND NOT DISASTER, PLANS TO BRING ABOUT THE FUTURE YOU HOPE FOR. THEN YOU WILL CALL TO ME. YOU WILL COME AND PRAY TO ME AND I WILL ANSWER YOU.
(JEREMIAH 29 V 11-12)

LET US HOLD FIRMLY TO THE HOPE WE PROFESS, BECAUSE WE CAN TRUST GOD TO KEEP HIS PROMISE.
(HEBREWS 10 V 23).

HE GIVETH POWER TO THE FAINT, AND TO THEM THAT HAVE NO MIGHT HE INCREASETH. STRENGTH.
(ISAIAH 60 V 29).

TRUST IN THE LORD WITH ALL THINE HEART AND LEAN NOT UNTO THINE OWN UNDERSTANDING.
(PROVERBS 3 V 5).

BEHOLD I AM THE LORD THE GOD OF ALL FLESH, IS THERE ANYTHING TOO HARD FOR ME.
(JEREMAIH 32 V 27).

THOU WILT KEEP HIM IN PERFECT PEACE WHOSE MIND IS STAYED ON THEE.
(ISAIAH 26 V 3).

COME UNTO ME ALL YE THAT LABOUR AND I WILL
GIVE YOU REST.
(MATHEW 11 V 28)

AND WE KNOW THAT ALL THINGS WORK
TOGETHER FOR GOOD TO THEM THAT LOVE
GOD, TO THEM WHO ARE CALLED ACCORDING
TO HIS PURPOSE.
(ROMANS 8 V 28)

...BUT THIS ONE THING I DO, FORGETTING THOSE
THINGS WHICH ARE BEHIND, AND REACHING
FORTH UNTO THOSE THINGS WHICH ARE BEFORE...
(PHILLIPIANS 3 V 13)

FOR WITH GOD NOTHING SHALL BE IMPOSSIBLE.
(LUKE 1 V 37)

SUBMIT YOURSELVES THEREFORE TO GOD. RESIST
THE DEVIL AND HE WILL FLEE FROM YOU. DRAW
NIGH TO GOD, AND HE WILL DRAW NIGH TO YOU...
(JAMES 4 V 7-8)

...GREATER IS HE THAT IS IN YOU, THAN HE THAT
IS IN THE WORLD.
(1 JOHN 4 V 4)

THY WORD HAVE I HID IN MINE HEART THAT I
MIGHT NOT SIN AGAINST THEE.
(PSALM 119 V 11)

THY WORD IS A LAMP UNTO MY FEET, AND A LIGHT UNTO MY PATH.
(PSALM 119 V 105)

MANY ARE THE AFFLICTIONS OF THE RIGHTEOUS: BUT THE LORD DELIVERETH HIM OUT OF THEM ALL.
(PSALM 34 V 19)

SEARCH ME O GOD, AND KNOW MY HEART: TRY ME, AND KNOW MY THOUGHTS: AND SEE IF THERE BE ANY WICKED WAY IN ME, AND LEAD ME IN THE WAY EVERLASTING.
(PSALM 139 V 23-24)

I strongly believe that soaking my mind with the above Bible verses, and more, helped me to come to terms with the devastating consequence of the illness known as sepsis. Indeed, they also helped me to heal emotionally, physically, and spiritually – and very quickly too.

Glory be to God in the Highest!

Chapter 13 –

A Harvest Of Motivational Thoughts

Thank you for reading this book. The story is my testimony to the indomitable human drive to survive, and the indestructible human will, that helps us to triumph in the face of adverse circumstances.

I sincerely hope that, whatever you are going through, this book provides you with the encouragement you need. Many friends have commented that seeing me rise up above my disability helped them to rise above their own challenging situations, and I pray that the same will be true for you. I was determined to make something out of my life after sepsis. I was determined to have new ambitions after I lost my legs. This determination motivated me to fight back. I set new goals for myself, including the writing of this book.

May I leave you with the following motivational thoughts, to ponder and act upon:

- Go out of your way to encourage people. By doing this, you help them to boost their self-esteem, enhance their self-confidence, and help lift their spirits. This singular act of yours goes straight to the other person's heart, so be an encourager as much as you can. Help others to move forward, and keep on keeping on, no matter how hard the circumstances. Believing that God is with you all the time makes you stronger and fearless, as you face your struggles in this life. Trust in God, and He will strengthen and comfort you in your time of need. So, stand firm in your faith and be encouraged. For it is well with you.

- Be grateful to people who put a smile on your face, as they are the God-sent, who will help to raise your spirit. Make someone's day today by appreciating them. Don't be shy to express your gratitude to them with kind words. Be thankful for your struggle, because without it you wouldn't have stumbled across your strength. Walk outside, stand still in silence. Look up to the sky and imagine how awesome and amazing our Creator – who made all things – is.

- Appreciate and love your life in order to feel the joy of living. Do not think about the possibility of death, or worry of others passing. Stop complaining about life, and live your own life to the best of your ability. Stress and worry don't solve problems, rather they block your attempts at creativity. Remember though, that every problem has a solution. Clear your mind and you will envisage the resolution. That problem, which looks insurmountable now, is the bridge between you and your goal. So, do everything within your power to get over that bridge. Be happy and enjoy every moment of your life, because you'll only live once. Time lost can never be regained.

- Fill your life with action to make things happen for you, for your future. Faith without work is nothing. Don't wait for grace to fall from heaven, by sitting down and doing nothing. Do what you can to make grace locate you.

- In life there will be sickness, bereavement, disappointment, and emotional upheavals, whatever you do. But the way you choose to get through these is what counts, and enables you to see that the grass is indeed greener on the other side. So, live your life to the fullest by being happy now – in the present. Don't dwell on the past, because it's gone forever. Similarly, do not worry about the future. Just keep working towards that goal.

- Use your God-given talents now, for His glory so that when you stand before God on the last day, you can say with all certainty, 'I used everything You gave me Lord.' Remember that everything that has happened to you, happened for a reason. You can either wallow in self-pity or treat what happened as another test of your faith. Choose the former, and you will never grow. Choose the latter, and you will get the opportunity to soar. Courage doesn't come without fear, but it's your judgement that counts. It's your judgement that tells you if you're onto something greater and more important than your fear.

- Follow your passion, and know what you really want and love to do. Then, have the courage to do it. The only courage you'll ever need is that which propels you to follow your dream.

- Always take the first step by faith, without seeing the light at the end of the tunnel. You will be amazed at how that light will come flowing towards you, as you start to reach the end of the journey.

Chapter 14 – GOFUNDME

I decided to write about GoFundMe for the benefit of those people who have never heard of it, or don't know how it works. I personally had never heard of GoFundMe, until I was required to find extra money to supplement the council grant for the building of an en-suite bedroom at the back of my house.

I contacted a solicitor friend – Miss Nicki Adesemowo (to whom I am very grateful) to find out if she knew any charities that I could approach for help. It was at this point that Nicki suggested raising the money through GoFundMe. She also introduced me to a gentleman, Mr Dapo Awosokanre, who advised me on how to make my appeal on GoFundMe, YouTube and Facebook. He then set everything up for me without charging a fee. My thanks go to him also.

What is GoFundMe?

GoFundMe is a for-profit crowdfunding platform that allows people to raise money for events ranging from life events such as celebrations and graduations to challenging circumstances like accidents and illnesses.

Here are the benefits of raising money via this platform. Namely, you get:

- Mobile-friendly campaigns.
- You don't have to pay any penalties for missing your goals.
- You can get the GoFundMe Mobile App.

- There are no deadlines or goal requirements.

- You have access to expert advice, 24/7.

- You get to keep every donation you receive.

How Can We Use GoFundMe to Fight Sepsis?

GoFundMe can serve as a vital tool in the war against sepsis. The only way that we will conquer this condition, and spread awareness, is to work together. Furthermore, not every country in the world has free healthcare. There are many countries that do not have a National Health Service, and this means that the cost of medical treatment for sepsis sufferers is alarmingly expensive. It means that even if sufferers do manage to conquer the disease, there is still a whole extra mountain to climb upon recovery – with enormous debts being accrued. GoFundMe can help with this. If you or anyone you know is suffering from sepsis, you can use this excellent platform to help raise money for their treatment.

Furthermore, even if you don't know someone who is suffering from the condition, you can still start a GoFundMe page today – with the aim of donating money to sepsis research and other such endeavours. The power is in our hands – so we must use technology to our advantage.

Acknowledgements

I would like to use this opportunity to thank all donors – known and unknown to me – for their kind donations. I would like to mention a few names here:

First and foremost, I would like to thank Mrs Folorunsho Alakija, who donated funds to my cause at the request of my friend Princess Teni Aofiyebi. I thank Teni also for mobilising members of my Alma Mater St. Anne's school both in Nigeria and here in the UK to rally round me and support me. I am very grateful to my classmates, juniors, and seniors for the contributions they made.

I thank the Ex-President of SSASOGA, UK, Mrs Abimbola Ope-ewe and the committee members who visited me at home and also donated funds to help me.

Many thanks to my first cousins – Professor Ladi Otolorin and his siblings for their donations.

My gratitude also goes to Mr Mike Abiola who published my story and pictures on the front page of the African Voice newspaper, thereby assisting me to raise the much needed funds. I also thank his church for the cheque they brought to me at my house.

I say a big thank you to:

The President and members of Sagamu Club, members of Young Men and Young Women Progress League of Ereko Methodist Church, Lagos.

Mr and Mrs Sam Bolarinde, Dr & Mrs Tunji Omotoso, Mr Remi Adetayo, Professor Kayode Dada, Shagamu Club,

Mr Adem Adewoyin, Mrs Gwen Ike Nwachukwu, Mrs Morin Desalu, Mrs Bernadette Yau, Dr Kola Ashaye, Late Prince Yiga & Mrs Tiwalade Benson, Mr & Mrs Abi Odojukan, Mr Tunde Soile, Prof Labi Somorin, Prince Kunle Adesanya, Chief Abiodun Onafuwa, Mr Yinka Odulate, Mrs Bimbo Talabi, Ms Femi Finnih, Mrs Kike Adeyemi, Mr Kunle Akinlabi, Mr & Mrs Tunde Carew, Mr Dipo Shodeinde, Mrs Moji Otolorin, Mrs Ranti Otolorin.

Ms Dotun Ademola, Mama Mrs Dawodu , Mrs Dupe Abiodun-Wright, Sister Bola(nee Osibodu), Mrs Sade Odunlami, Mrs Tokunbo Adetunji, Mrs Molade Bello, Mrs Stella Ajayi, Ms Yinka Payne, Mr Olubayiwa Sosina, Mr Tunji Okulaja, Mrs Bisi Asimolowo, Dr Christie Aboaba, Mr & Mrs Olumide Ayodele, Mrs Mojoyinola Ojediran, Mrs Gladys Lemoh, Ms Yetty Adegbite, Mr & Mrs Dele Ogunnaike, Princess Adeyinka Adedoyin, Ms Antonia Justin, Ms Bunmi Osoba and children.

I thank all other donors and anonymous donors too numerous to mention. God bless you all.

Finally, I also wish to extend my sincere gratitude to all staff at the Accident & Emergency dept, Intensive Care Unit, Plastics dept and McKentee Ward of St George's Hospital, Staff of Queen Mary's Hospital, Roehampton for their care during and after my illness.

My gratitude also goes to the Pastoral team at Kensington Temple, Nottinghill Gate, London.

Printed in Poland
by Amazon Fulfillment
Poland Sp. z o.o., Wrocław

49278927R00130